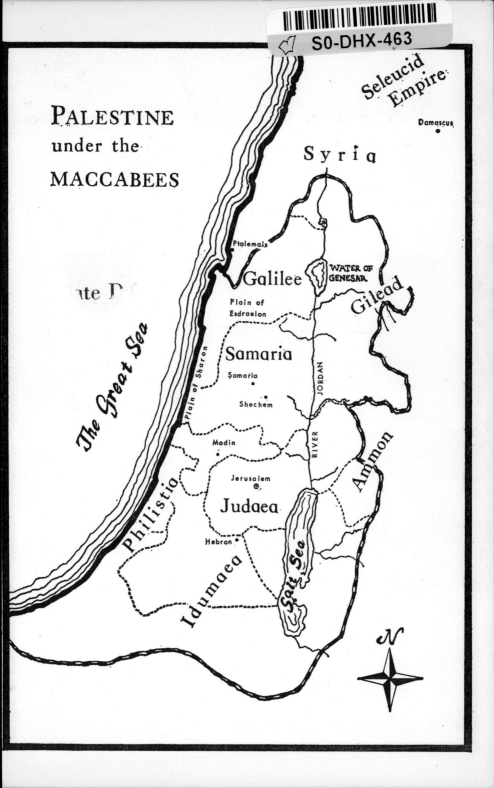

# PALESTINE
## under the
## MACCABEES

Seleucid Empire

Damascus

Syria

Ptolemais

Galilee

WATER OF GENESAR

Gilead

Plain of Esdraelon

The Great Sea

ate D

Plain of Sharon

Samaria

Samaria

Shechem

JORDAN RIVER

Modin

Jerusalem

Ammon

Judaea

Philistia

Hebron

Idumaea

Salt Sea

N

# THE THREE GUARDSMEN

and Other Stories from the Apocrypha

# The Three Guardsmen

## and Other Stories from the Apocrypha

EDITH PATTERSON MEYER

*Illustrations by Howard Simon*

*New York*   ABINGDON PRESS   *Nashville*

*To my nieces and nephews—the parents of the children
to whom* Bible Stories for Young Readers *is dedicated*

# CONTENTS

# ACKNOWLEDGMENT

I wish to express my sincere thanks to Rabbi David W. Pearlman, Monsignor John J. Hayes, and the Reverend Dr. Russell M. McGown, all of Stamford, for their critical reading of this book in manuscript form and for their encouragement and help.

The Author

## AUTHOR'S NOTE

There's a time gap between the Old and New Testaments—four hundred years of exciting history, interesting stories, and rich wisdom. Part of this history, some of the stories, and much of the wisdom are set down in the fifteen books called the Apocrypha—the "hidden" or "outside" books of the Old Testament. Some of them were written just before the time of Christ; others, during or not long after it.

Probably Jesus knew some of the Apocrypha books well; certainly the Apostle Paul did. We know they were of comfort to the early Christians, for scenes from these books were painted in the underground catacombs where the followers of Christ hid from their Roman persecutors. The Apocrypha books were included in Christian Bibles and read in Christian church services for hundreds of years, along with the books of the Old Testament. Then, gradually, they were dropped from Protestant Bibles. If you are interested in knowing how this happened, and how these "outside" books came to be in the Bible in the first place, turn to the chapter "About the Apocrypha," at the end of this book.

As you read these stories from the Apocrypha, you can decide for yourself how important you think they are. I hope you will agree with me that they are far too good to be forgotten.

Edith Patterson Meyer

Stamford, Connecticut
October, 1959

## THE THREE GUARDSMEN

The first book of the Apocrypha, 1 Esdras, covers the same history as the Old Testament books of II Chronicles, Ezra, and Nehemiah. It tells of the temple worship in the days of Judah's good King Josiah, of the capture of Jerusalem by the Babylonians, of the return of the Jewish captives from Babylon and their rebuilding of the temple. It also tells about their scribe, whose name was Ezra—or Esdras, as the name is in Greek.

But there is a story in the book of Esdras that is not given in the Old Testament books. It is the story of the three guardsmen.

11

The great Darius, king of Persia, Media, Assyria, and Babylonia, once gave a grand banquet for his nobles and generals and governors. When it was over, King Darius left the great hall and went to his bedroom.

Three young men were in the room to guard the king. These young men were strong and loyal and brave. They were also ambitious. Each of them wanted many things, favors that only a powerful king could grant. After King Darius was in bed and asleep, the three young guardsmen whispered together and made a plan. They decided to have a contest among themselves and ask the king to judge it. They thought he might give the winner rich gifts and grant him the favors he wanted.

The young guardsmen imagined great things. The winner of the contest might, they thought, "be clothed in purple, and drink from gold cups, and sleep on a gold bed, and have a chariot with gold bridles, and a turban of fine linen, and a necklace about his neck; and because of his wisdom he shall sit next to Darius and shall be called kinsman of Darius."

For the contest they agreed that each of them should write down what he believed to be the strongest thing in the whole world. Each guardsman would then fold and seal his statement and slip it under the sleeping king's pillow. When Darius awoke, they would ask him to read what they had written and decide which statement was the wisest. The one who had written it would be the winner of the contest.

The first young man wrote: "Wine is strongest."

The second young man wrote: "The king is strongest."

The third young man wrote: "Women are strongest, but truth is victor over all things."

The guardsmen put their statements under the sleeping king's pillow. Then they sat about, waiting for morning.

At last King Darius awoke, and the young men explained their plan. To their delight, the king agreed to judge the contest. But he wanted the help of the men who had been his guests at the banquet the night before. So he sent for them to come to the council room.

When all the guests were gathered in the great hall, the king entered and took his seat. He ordered the seals on the guardsmen's secret statements to be broken and the statements read. After the reading, King Darius said, "Call the young men, and they shall explain their statements."

The three young men came in. The first one—the one who had written: "Wine is strongest"—spoke of the strength of wine. "Wine," he said, "leads astray the minds of all who drink it. . . . When men drink they forget to be friendly with friends and brothers, and before long they draw their swords. And when they recover from the wine, they do not remember what they have done. Gentlemen," the young man concluded, "is not wine the strongest, since it forces men to do these things?"

Then the second young man—the one who had written: "The king is strongest"—spoke. He reminded his listeners that whatever the king told his people to do they had to do. "If he tells them to attack, they attack, if he tells them to lay waste, they lay waste; if he tells them to build, they build; if he tells them to cut down, they cut down; if he tells them to plant, they plant. All his people and his armies obey him." The second young man ended his speech, "Gentlemen, why is not the king the strongest, since he is to be obeyed in this fashion?"

The third young man, whose name was Zerubbabel, was the one who had written: "Women are strongest, but truth is victor over all things." Zerubbabel agreed that wine was strong and the king was strong. But women, he pointed out, were even stronger. "Women brought up the very men who plant the vineyards from which comes wine. Women make men's clothes; they bring men glory; men cannot exist without women. . . . A man leaves his own father, who brought him up, and his own country, and cleaves to his wife. . . . Do you not labor and toil, and bring everything and give it to women?" Zerubbabel asked the nobles. Even the king, he said, was influenced by a woman. "If she smiles at him, he laughs; if she loses her temper with him, he flatters her, that she may be reconciled to him. Gentlemen," said Zerubbabel, "why are not women strong, since they do such things?"

The king and the nobles looked at one another and nodded. But before the king had a chance to speak, Zerubbabel continued. "But truth is great, and stronger than all things. . . . Truth . . . lives and prevails for ever

and ever. . . . . To her belongs the strength and the king-
ship and the power and the majesty of all the ages. Blessed
be the God of truth!" And Zerubbabel bowed low to the
king and sat down.

The king and the nobles and the generals and governors
clapped their hands and shouted their approval. "Great
is truth," they cried, "and strongest of all!"

Then King Darius said to the third young guardsman,
"Ask what you wish, even beyond what is written, and
we will give it to you, for you have been found to be the
wisest. And you shall sit next to me, and be called my
kinsman."

It did not take Zerubbabel long to decide what to ask
the king. He was one of the captive Jews in Darius' kingdom. He had heard what a hard time the Jews who had
returned to Jerusalem some years before were having
there. They were trying to rebuild their city and their
temple, but they were poor and the work was going slowly.
Instead of asking for something for himself, Zerubbabel
reminded Darius of a promise he had made when he had
become king. He had vowed then to help the Jews rebuild
their temple in Jerusalem and to send back the holy
vessels used in it.

"And now, O lord the king," said Zerubbabel, "this is
what I ask and request of you, and this befits your greatness. I pray therefore that you fulfil the vow whose fulfilment you vowed to the King of heaven with your own
lips."

King Darius was pleased with the young man's request. He rose and embraced him. Then he called a scribe, and he began at once to dictate letters to important persons who could help in this big undertaking. He wrote to his governor in Lebanon asking him to send cedar timbers to Jerusalem. He ordered the people who held Jewish villages captive to give them up. He taxed other villages for the building of the temple, and he arranged for the support of the temple priests and for the return of the temple vessels. Finally he promised freedom and a safe journey to any Jews who wanted to go from Babylon to help rebuild Jerusalem. Everything that Zerubbabel asked—and more—Darius did.

"When the young man went out, he lifted up his face to heaven toward Jerusalem, and praised the King of heaven, saying, 'From thee is the victory; from thee is wisdom; and thine is the glory. I am thy servant. Blessed art thou, who hast given me wisdom; I give thee thanks, O Lord of our fathers.' "

Zerubbabel took the letters the king had written and hurried to the city of Babylon. There he told the good news to the many Jews who lived there. They, too, praised God "and they feasted, with music and rejoicing, for seven days." Then they chose men to lead those who wanted to make the long journey back to Jerusalem.

And when the people left, "Darius sent with them a thousand horsemen to take them back to Jerusalem in safety, with the music of drums and flutes."

16

## SOME CURIOUS VISIONS

Long ago, people used to pay more attention to dreams than most people do today. Every part of a dream had a meaning. Strange animals and wild weather and dreadful happenings all stood for things that had taken place in the past or would take place in the future.

There are many dreams and visions in our Bible. Abraham, Joseph, Moses, Daniel, the prophets, and many others dreamed dreams and saw visions. The Apostle Peter had a vision on the housetop at Joppa; and the whole of the last book of the New Testament, The Revelation to John, is a vision of the things to come.

2 Esdras, in the Apocrypha, tells of not just one vision but of seven. It was written much later than most of the Apocrypha books, probably about a hundred years after Jesus' birth, and its beginning and ending were added by early Christian writers. But the author pretended to be the scribe Ezra, writing in the days of the Jews' captivity four centuries before Christ.

The reason for this was that 2 Esdras was written in a time of persecution. By seeming to write about a vision in a time long past, the author could say things he did not dare to say openly. The Roman rulers did not know that when the writer of 2 Esdras said Babylon he really meant Rome, or that he used the fierce eagle to stand for the Roman Empire. But the Jewish people who read the vision or heard it read knew, and they could see in it what the author meant them to see. They understood that he was warning them against dangers about them and troubles ahead. They knew that he was writing to comfort and cheer them, to plead with them to do right, and to trust God to bring about a better world.

Ezra—or Esdras, as the Greeks would call him—was troubled. He was so troubled that when he lay down he could not sleep. It seemed to him that God had commanded him to speak sternly to the people of Israel. He was to tell them that, because they had broken God's commandments and had not listened to the prophets, God was going to give to others the high place he had planned for Israel.

Scribe Ezra turned and twisted on his bed. Why should

this happen to the people of Israel? he wondered. Why not to the Babylonians? They were much worse than the Hebrews. The Babylonians even worshiped idols. Yet they grew rich and powerful while the Hebrews suffered.

Then it seemed to Ezra that God sent an angel to reason with him. And the angel said to Ezra, "I have been sent to show you three ways, and to put before you three problems. If you can solve one of them for me, I also will show you the way you desire to see." And the angel went on, "Go, weigh for me the weight of fire, or measure for me a measure of wind, or call back for me the day that is past."

"Who of those that have been born can do this?" Ezra answered.

"I have asked you only about fire and wind and the day," the angel said, "things through which you have passed and without which you cannot exist, and you have given me no answer about them. . . . You cannot understand the things with which you have grown up; how then can your mind comprehend the way of the Most High?"

This did not silence Ezra, nor did other arguments that the angel presented. Why had he been given a mind, Ezra thought, if not to use it? He was determined to find out why God was letting the people of Israel suffer.

The angel told Ezra that God knew he was sincere and good, and much disturbed about Israel's sufferings. "Therefore he sent me to show you all these things, and to say to you: 'Believe and do not be afraid!' " And the

19

angel added that some of Ezra's questions would be answered through visions.

Then Ezra had several curious visions. In one of them he seemed to talk with a woman who was mourning for her dead son. Ezra told her that since the grief of Israel was far greater than her grief, she should bear her troubles bravely. After they had talked together for a long time a change came over the woman. Her face began to shine and to flash like lightning. Ezra was terrified. Suddenly the woman vanished, and where she had stood, Ezra saw a great city. The angel explained that the woman was the city of Zion—Jerusalem—and that the death of her son was the destruction of Jerusalem. But the city Ezra was seeing was the great city that would be—the holy city of Zion.

In another vision Ezra saw a three-headed eagle rise out of the sea. The eagle gained control of the whole earth and ruled over it. Then a creature like a lion came roaring out of the woods. Speaking in a man's voice the lion rebuked the eagle for its crimes. As the lion spoke, little by little the eagle disappeared until it was completely gone. The eagle, the angel explained, was a great kingdom, and the lion was the Messiah that God had promised to send to deliver his people from their troubles.

Ezra had many strange visions and dreams, and each one strengthened his faith in God. He wanted to pass his faith and his new knowledge on to the people. So he gathered them around him and he said to them: "Take courage, O Israel; and do not be sorrowful, O house of Jacob; for the Most High has you in remembrance, and the Mighty One has not forgotten you in your struggle." And he told them of the things he had learned.

One day it seemed to Ezra that God spoke to him again. This time God told him to take five scribes who had been trained to write rapidly and to go away to a quiet place for forty days. "And I will light in your heart the lamp of understanding, which shall not be put out until what you are about to write is finished. And when you have finished, some things you shall make public, and some you shall deliver in secret to the wise."

Ezra chose five good scribes and collected writing tablets and other things they would need. Then the six men went away to a quiet place.

The next day Ezra seemed to hear a voice saying, "Ezra, open your mouth and drink what I give you to drink."

Ezra saw before him a cup "full of something like water, but its color was like fire." He took the cup and drank what was in it. Immediately he was filled with wisdom and understanding.

Then Ezra began to dictate. He dictated to the five men by turns, and they wrote down what he said. They wrote in characters which they did not know, for God had given them strange powers, too. For forty days Ezra dictated all day long and sometimes far into the night, while the scribes wrote and wrote. They did not even stop to eat until it was dark.

At the end of the forty days, ninety-four books had been written. Then God said to Ezra, "Make public the twenty-four books that you wrote first and let the worthy and the unworthy read them; but keep the seventy that were written last, in order to give them to the wise among your people. For in them is the spring of understanding, the fountain of wisdom, and the river of knowledge." And that was what Ezra did.

As long as he was able, Ezra went on preaching to the people. He told them that in spite of the troubles that lay ahead—famine, wars, and calamities—they should never forget God or lose hope in him. "For behold, just a little while, and iniquity will be removed from the earth, and righteousness will reign over us."

# THE STRANGE ADVENTURES OF TOBIAS

In the early 1950's a few Arabian boys found some old scrolls in caves near the Dead Sea. Among these ancient Dead Sea Scrolls were bits of a story popular with the Jews of Jesus' time and even earlier, the story of Tobit and his son Tobias. This story was so well liked that it was written many times in many different languages and was known to people in many lands. It was read by people in Hebrew, Aramaic (the language Jesus spoke), Greek, and even in the Syrian and Ethiopian tongues. In the ancient British wedding ceremony Tobias and his bride Sarah were mentioned as a model couple.

Tobit lived in Galilee with his wife Anna and their son Tobias until the Assyrians captured the country. Then Tobit and his family were taken from their homes and, with many other Hebrews, led as captives to the faraway Assyrian city of Nineveh. Most of the Hebrews were treated fairly well there, and some of them got along very nicely. Tobit was one of the fortunate captives. He became a buyer for the king, a very responsible position.

Tobit's work required him to make long journeys, sometimes even to other countries. On one of these trips Tobit turned over some of the money he had made to a man who lived in Rages in Media. This man, whose name was Gabael, agreed to keep the money in trust for Tobit.

Tobit was a good and pious man. He was kind and generous, and was always giving money and food and clothing to those who needed it. And when, as sometimes happened, one of the captive Hebrews was murdered and his body thrown behind the city wall, Tobit would secretly rescue the body and bury it.

All went well for Tobit until the Assyrian king for whom he was buyer died and a cruel king took his place. Then there were many more murders of the captive Hebrews. The cruel king learned of Tobit's pious habit of burying the Hebrew bodies and it made him so angry that he ordered Tobit put to death. Tobit heard of the order and hurriedly left his home and went into hiding. When the king's men could not find Tobit, they took everything he owned, but left Anna and Tobias unharmed.

Before long the cruel king was murdered and his son, a much better man, became king. The new king appointed a nephew of Tobit as his cupbearer and the keeper of all his accounts. This nephew got the king's consent for Tobit to leave his hiding place and return to his family in Nineveh.

It was Pentecost feast time when Tobit came home. His wife Anna prepared a big dinner in celebration of his return. The good Tobit, seeing so much food, wanted to share it with others. So he said to his son Tobias, "Go and bring whatever poor man of our brethren you may find who is mindful of the Lord, and I will wait for you."

Tobias went out but very soon came rushing back, alone and breathless. "Father," he said, "one of our people has been strangled and thrown into the market place."

Before he ate a mouthful, Tobit rushed out and rescued the body. Then he returned, washed, and sadly ate his food. After dark he dug a grave and buried the body. The neighbors saw, and thought Tobit was foolish to do again the very thing that had almost cost him his life.

That night when Tobit returned from burying the dead man he slept outside in the court. He did this because according to the Hebrew rules he followed he was unclean from touching the dead body. As Tobit lay in the court, droppings from the sparrows in the courtyard fell into his eyes, blinding him. He could not see a thing! No doctor could help him, and nothing he did brought back his sight.

Poor blind Tobit could find no work. For a time the nephew in the king's service supported Tobit and his family. Then the nephew was sent to another city, and Anna earned money for the family by sewing for wealthy women.

One day one of the women gave Anna a small goat in addition to her pay. When she brought it home, Tobit heard the little goat bleat. "Where did you get the kid?" he asked. "It is not stolen, is it?"

When Anna told Tobit that the little goat was a gift, he would not believe her. He told her to return it to the owner. This upset Anna, and she spoke sharply to her husband. Tobit, weary of his blindness and uselessness and feeling himself a burden, wept. Better be dead than alive this way, he thought.

As he sat there moping, Tobit suddenly remembered the money he had left with Gabael in Rages. During the cruel king's reign the highways had been too dangerous for him to make the journey there; then he had been in hiding; and then he had become blind. But if he were going to die, someone should go and get the money. That someone would have to be his son. Tobias was old enough now, Tobit decided, to make the long journey to Media.

Tobit called Tobias and first gave him advice. He told Tobias how he should live when he no longer had a father: he should honor his mother and not grieve or neglect her; he should give to the needy, pay his debts promptly, seek and follow advice from wise men, and love his brethren. "And what you hate," said Tobit, "do not do to any one." Tobit also advised Tobias not to marry a foreign woman but to choose a wife from among the Hebrew people.

Then Tobit explained to his son about the money left with Gabael, and told Tobias how to get it. "Do not be afraid, my son, because we have become poor," said Tobit. "You have great wealth if you fear God and refrain from every sin and do what is pleasing in his sight."

"Father, I will do everything that you have commanded me," Tobias answered; "but how can I obtain the money when I do not know the man?"

Tobit gave his son the receipt he had saved for many years. Then he said, "Find a man to go with you and I will pay him wages as long as I live."

So Tobias went out to look for a companion, and he found Raphael. Raphael was an angel, but Tobias did not know this. "Can you go with me to Rages in Media?" Tobias asked. "Are you acquainted with that region?"

Raphael answered, "I will go with you; I am familiar with the way."

Tobias was pleased. "Wait for me, and I shall tell my father," he said. And he hurried home to tell his father that he had found someone to go with him.

"Call him to me," said Tobit, "so that I may learn to what tribe he belongs, and whether he is a reliable man to go with you."

Tobias brought Raphael to Tobit, and they greeted

each other. Tobit asked Raphael what tribe and family he belonged to. At this, Raphael seemed annoyed. "Are you looking for a tribe and a family or for a man whom you will pay to go with your son?" he asked. But when Tobit insisted, Raphael gave as his name the name of a distant relative of Tobit. This connection pleased Tobit and made him feel more secure about Tobias' companion. He offered to pay Raphael's expenses and to give him a drachma a day and an additional sum when the two were safely back.

Raphael agreed, and so it was settled. "Get ready for the journey, and good success to you both," said Tobit. And when they left he said to his son, "Go with this man; God who dwells in heaven will prosper your way, and may his angel attend you."

Tobias and Raphael started out. As they turned into the highway, Tobias' little dog bounded out of the house and ran along beside them. Anna wept to see her son go. She scolded Tobit for sending Tobias on such a long, dangerous journey just to get some money. Tobit told her not to worry. "A good angel will go with him," he said; "his journey will be successful, and he will come back safe and sound." And Anna believed her husband and stopped crying.

Tobias and Raphael walked all day. When evening came, they camped beside a river, and Tobias jumped into it to bathe. As he splashed about, a great fish leaped up out of the water.

"Catch the fish!" Raphael shouted. Tobias seized the big fish and threw it up on the land. "Cut open the fish and take the heart and the liver and gall and put them away safely," Raphael directed. Tobias did this. Then he and Raphael made a fire and roasted the fish and ate it.

The next day as they walked along Tobias asked why they were saving the fish liver and heart and gall. "As for the heart and the liver," Raphael said, "if a demon or evil spirit gives trouble to any one, you make a smoke from these before the man or woman, and that person will never be troubled again. And as for the gall, anoint with it a man who has white films in his eyes, and he will be cured."

The way to Rages led through the city of Ecbatana. As they drew near the city, Raphael said to Tobias, "Brother, today we shall stay with Raguel. He is your relative, and he has an only daughter named Sarah. I will suggest that she be given to you in marriage, because you are entitled to her and to her inheritance, for you are her only eligible kinsman. The girl is also beautiful and sensible. Now listen to my plan. I will speak to her father, and as soon as we return from Rages we will celebrate the marriage."

Tobias was not too sure that this was a good idea. He had heard some astonishing things about his distant cousin Sarah. Seven times her parents had given her in marriage; and each time, immediately after the wedding, an evil spirit who was in love with Sarah had slain the bridegroom. Tobias had no desire to be the eighth victim! "I fear that I may die and bring the lives of my father and mother to the grave in sorrow on my account," he complained to Raphael.

Raphael reminded Tobias of his father's advice to take a wife from among his own people. "Do not worry about the demon," he said. "When you enter the bridal chamber, you shall take live ashes of incense and lay upon them some of the heart and liver of the fish so as to make a smoke. Then the demon will smell it and flee away, and will never again return. . . . Do not be afraid, for she was destined for you from eternity. You will save her, and she will go with you."

Tobias was relieved. He believed Raphael, and now he became eager to meet Sarah. Already he felt that he was beginning to be in love with her.

When they reached Ecbatana, they went to Raguel's home. Sarah greeted them and took them into the house.

"How much the young man resembles my cousin Tobit!" Raguel said to his wife Edna. "Where are you from, brethren?"

"We belong to the sons of Naphtali, who are captives in Nineveh," said Tobias.

"Do you know our brother Tobit?" Raguel asked.

"Yes," answered Tobias and Raphael, "we do."

"Is he in good health?"

"He is alive and in good health," said Raphael and Tobias together.

Then Tobias could be silent no longer. "He is my father," he said.

"Son of that good and noble man!" Raguel exclaimed, and he embraced Tobias. When Tobias told Raguel that Tobit had lost his sight, Raguel wept, and Edna and Sarah wept with him.

Raguel and Edna did everything possible for Tobias' and Raphael's comfort. They even ordered their servants to kill a ram from the flock and to prepare a fine dinner in honor of their guests.

Tobias asked Raphael not to wait any longer to do what he had suggested, but to arrange the matter of the marriage at once. So Raphael spoke to Sarah's father about it.

Raguel agreed that it was Tobias' right, as kinsman, to marry Sarah. "But," he said honestly, "let me explain the true situation to you." And he told them of the seven husbands who had died mysteriously on their wedding night. He sighed, then urged Tobias to forget all this for the moment and to eat and be merry.

But Tobias, who by now was really in love with Sarah, said, "I will eat nothing here until you make a binding agreement with me."

Then Raguel took Sarah by the hand and gave her to Tobias to be his wife, and he blessed them. He wrote the marriage contract on a scroll, and he and Edna set their seals to it. After this the five of them sat down to eat.

Sarah had been deeply upset by the tragic death of the seven bridegrooms. Thinking of her past experiences and dreading what was almost surely ahead, she began to weep. Her mother took her aside to comfort her. "The Lord of heaven and earth grant you joy in place of this sorrow of yours," Edna said. "Be brave, my daughter."

As soon as Tobias and Sarah were alone together, Tobias put the fish heart and liver upon the live incense ashes. They sent up a great smoke and a dreadful smell. The demon, who appeared as Sarah had feared he would do, gave one sniff, smelled the odor, and fled away.

Tobias and Sarah were almost overcome with joy and relief, and they prayed to God to ask him to have mercy on them. Tobias prayed that he and Sarah might have a good life as man and wife and grow old together, and Sarah said *Amen*. Then they lay down and slept in peace.

Raguel did not know about the fish liver and heart. He kept thinking about the fate of the seven bridegrooms; and when Tobias and Sarah went to their room, he went outside and sadly dug a grave for Tobias. When he learned that Tobias was alive and well, Raguel was very glad. He offered a prayer of thanksgiving to God:
"Blessed art thou, because thou hast made me glad.
It has not happened to me as I expected;
but thou hast treated us according to thy great mercy.
Blessed art thou, because thou hast had compassion
on two only children.
Show them mercy, O Lord;
and bring their lives to fulfilment
in health and happiness and mercy."

The next day everyone at Raguel's house was smiling and happy. Raguel and Edna insisted on giving a wedding feast for the young couple. There was music and dancing and delicious food, and many friends coming and going. The feast lasted for fourteen days, and during that time Raguel gave Tobias and Sarah half of his property as a wedding present. The rest of it would go to them after Raguel's and Edna's deaths.

Before the feast was over, Tobias thought of his parents and realized how worried they must be about him. So he asked Raphael to take a servant and two camels and go on to Rages to get the money from Gabael. Tobias gave his father's receipt to Raphael and at Raguel's suggestion, told him to bring Gabael back with him to the wedding feast.

Raphael made the journey from Ecbatana to Rages so quickly that within a few days he was back, bringing Gabael and the money. Gabael had given it to Raphael without any trouble when he presented Tobit's receipt.

Raguel did his best to persuade Tobias to stay on in Ecbatana after the wedding feast was over. He promised to send messengers to Nineveh to tell Tobit and Anna that all was well with their son. But Tobias' mind was made up; he told Raguel and Edna that he and his bride must leave.

When Raguel saw that he could not keep the young couple, he gave them half his property, as he had promised. Then he kissed his daughter fondly, and said to her, "Honor your father-in-law and your mother-in-law; they are now your parents. Let me hear a good report of you." Edna, too, kissed Sarah and, turning to Tobias, begged him to take good care of her only daughter.

After the good-bys were said, Tobias and Sarah and Raphael started out. The dog ran along beside them. When they reached Nineveh, Raphael suggested that he and Tobias go on ahead. And he reminded Tobias to take the fish gall with them. They told Sarah to wait at the city gate, promising to come back for her soon. Then Tobias and Raphael hurried to Tobit's house.

Anna, watching beside the road as she had done every day for weeks, caught sight of them. She rushed back to the house to tell Tobit the good news. "Behold, your son is coming," she called, "and so is the man who went with him!" Then she hurried out to meet them. She hugged Tobias and wept for joy.

As Tobit tried to follow Anna out of the house to greet Tobias, he stumbled over the doorstep. Tobias, seeing him fall, pulled himself away from his mother and ran to help his father. Then, following Raphael's instructions, he sprinkled the fish gall on Tobit's sightless eyes.

The gall made Tobit's eyes smart, and he put his hand up to rub them. As he rubbed, the film fell away from his eyes. He looked up and saw his son for the first time in eight long years. Full of joy and thanksgiving, Tobit blessed the name of the Lord, then put his arms around

Tobias. And then the three went into the house, filled with happiness. There Tobias reported all the wonderful things that had happened to him on the journey.

Tobit and Anna were overjoyed to hear about their new daughter-in-law. Anna insisted on staying home to fix up the house while Tobit went back with Tobias to the city gate to greet Sarah. As he walked along, Tobit sang aloud his thanks to God. His neighbors heard him and looked out from their houses. They were delighted that blind Tobit could see again, and that his son was safely home.

Tobit greeted Sarah warmly. "Welcome, daughter!" he said. "Blessed is God who has brought you to us, and blessed are your father and your mother."

Sarah walked back through the city streets beside her husband and her new father-in-law. Once more the neighbors looked out from their houses and chatted to one another about Tobias' good fortune and Tobit's recovery.

Anna welcomed Sarah with love. Tobit and Anna also gave a wedding feast for the young couple. They invited their relatives, including the nephew in the king's service, and they all came. The feasting at this second wedding party went on for seven days.

Then Tobit thought of something important, which had been overlooked in their excitement over Sarah. "My son," Tobit said to Tobias, "see to the wages of the man who went with you; and he must also be given more."

"Father," Tobias said, "it would do me no harm to give

35

him half of what I have brought back. For he has led me back to you safely, he cured my wife, he obtained the money for me, and he also healed you."

Tobit nodded. "He deserves it," he agreed. And he called Raphael to him and said, "Take half of all that you two have brought back."

But Raphael told Tobit and Tobias that he wished to speak to them privately. Taking them aside he first instructed them always to praise God and give thanks to him. "Do good," said Raphael, "and evil will not overtake you. Prayer is good when accompanied by fasting, almsgiving, and righteousness." Then Raphael revealed to them that he was not an ordinary human being, as they had thought, but an angel. "God sent me to heal you and your daughter-in-law Sarah," he said to Tobit.

Tobit and Tobias were astonished. Filled with fear, they fell on their faces before Raphael.

"Do not be afraid," the angel said, "you will be safe. But praise God for ever. For I did not come as a favor on my part, but by the will of our God."

After directing them to "write in a book everything that has happened," Raphael left them, going back to God. And Tobit and Tobias never saw him again.

Tobit lived to a great old age. Never again was he blind or in need, and he always remembered the angel's advice to pray and do good to others. Before his death Tobit advised Tobias to leave Nineveh and take his wife and the sons they now had back to Media to live. For Nineveh,

Tobit was sure, would be destroyed, as the prophet Jonah had foretold.

After his father's and mother's death Tobias did move his family to Media. There, in Ecbatana, where Raguel and Edna lived, Tobias and Sarah and their sons lived happily for many years. They were wealthy, for Tobias and Sarah inherited Raguel's property as well as Tobit's. And Tobias "grew old with honor." He was thankful that he had taken his family to Media, for before his death he heard of the destruction of the city of Nineveh, as his father had warned.

## THE DARING DEED OF A BEAUTIFUL WOMAN

This story of Judith is not history, although it sounds as if it were. We know this, because the names of people and places do not agree with those connected with the events which occurred in the countries east of the Mediterranean Sea in ancient times. Probably the author of Judith put some actual happenings in his story to make it sound more real. At the time the book was written, the Jews were again being threatened by foreign kings, and he wanted to tell a heroic tale that would inspire them to trust in God and to fight their enemies to the death, in order to keep the true religion alive.

In the twelfth year of his reign Nebuchadnezzar, mighty king of Assyria, decided to make war against the king of Media. And Nebuchadnezzar commanded all the countries around Assyria to send armies and supplies to help him win the war. Many countries obeyed his command, but those to the west sent Nebuchadnezzar's messengers back empty handed.

In spite of this, Nebuchadnezzar won his war against Media. But he was very angry that the western countries had not obeyed his command, and he determined to destroy them. He called in his chief general, Holofernes, and put him in charge of the campaign.

"Take with you men confident in their strength, to the number of one hundred and twenty thousand foot soldiers and twelve thousand cavalry," Nebuchadnezzar directed Holofernes. "Go and attack the whole west country, because they disobeyed my orders."

Holofernes did as he was commanded. He marched westward with his troops, followed by camels and donkeys loaded with supplies. He killed many people in the western countries, took many captives, and forced the best soldiers of the conquered nations into his own army. In some of the countries the people were so frightened when Holofernes' army approached that they did not even try to defend themselves. They went out to meet their conquerors, singing and dancing and throwing flowers in their path. To escape death they agreed to everything the Assyrian general demanded, even to giving up their religion and worshiping King Nebuchadnezzar as a god.

At last Holofernes moved his army to a great plain in order to get his supplies together and reorganize the army after its long, successful march.

The plain of Esdraelon where the Assyrian army settled down was at the edge of the mountainous country of Judea. The Hebrews, who lived in Judea, knew that the Assyrian general would plan to come into their country next, and they were afraid. They were afraid not only for themselves but for their temple in Jerusalem which had just been rebuilt and rededicated to God. They could not bear to have a foreign army come in and destroy it. Neither would they consider saving themselves by promising to worship an earthly king, like Nebuchadnezzar. They knew that they were God's special people, and they were willing to die rather than stop worshiping him, the one true God.

In Jerusalem the high priest and the Hebrew senate met. They talked over the situation and decided to defy the Assyrians. They sent messengers to all parts of Judea, telling the people of the danger and ordering them to close all roads leading into their country. Each city and town was directed to store up the grain which had just been harvested, in case of a siege. All hilltop towns were to be fortified, especially Bethulia which overlooked the plain of Esdraelon, where Holofernes' army was camped. The men of Bethulia were ordered to guard the passes there and to keep the foreign army from using the narrow mountain paths which led up from the Esdraelon plain.

Holofernes was very angry when he heard that the mountain passes of Judea were closed to him and the hilltops fortified. He called in some of the men he had taken into his army from nearby countries. "What people is this that lives in the hill country?" he asked them. "What cities do they inhabit? How large is their army, and in what does their power or strength consist? Who rules over them as king, leading their army? And why have they alone, of all who live in the west, refused to come out and meet me?"

Achior, leader of the Ammonites, tried to answer Holofernes' questions. He told the general that the people of Israel worshiped a different God from the nations around them. He explained that everything went well for the Hebrews as long as they lived the way their God wanted them to live. But if they sinned against him, their God would punish them. Achior suggested to Holofernes that he try to find out some way in which the Hebrews had sinned against their God, for only then could they be defeated. "But if there is no transgression in their nation, then let my lord pass them by," Holofernes concluded; "for their Lord will defend them, and their God will protect them, and we shall be put to shame before the whole world."

Holofernes did not like Achior's suggestion. He could not believe that any power was greater than the army of Nebuchadnezzar. Why should he, an Assyrian general,

41

fear the people of Israel or their God? Achior, Holofernes decided, should soon see for himself! And he told his men to take the Ammonite soldier and leave him beside one of the mountain passes. Then, when the Assyrian army took the pass, as Holofernes was sure it would do, Achior would die along with the people of Israel, who dared defy Nebuchadnezzar and his general.

Holofernes' men bound Achior and led him across the plain. When they reached the springs below Bethulia, the men guarding the hills above saw them and hurled down stones. Leaving Achior, Holofernes' men hurried away.

When the guardsmen from Bethulia saw that there was only one man by the springs, they scrambled down the mountain path to him. They untied the bound man, led him up into the town, and took him before their rulers, Uzziah and Chabris and Charmis.

The people of Bethulia gathered around to hear what Achior had to say. When he repeated what he had told Holofernes, the people cheered him. The rulers praised him, too; and Uzziah took Achior to his home and gave a feast for him.

The next day the army of Holofernes moved closer to Bethulia and camped just below the city. The size of the army spread out over the plain terrified the people of Judea. Yet every man bravely took up his weapons, ready to fight for his country and his God. In the hilltop towns watch fires were kindled in the towers, and men remained on guard all night. But Holofernes did not attack. Instead, he seized the springs that supplied Bethulia with drinking water. He closed off the paths so that no one could escape from the town or bring help into it. Then he and his army settled down to wait until the people in the hill town surrendered or died of thirst and starvation.

Each day there was less food and less water for the people of Bethulia. After a month the cisterns went dry and the water that had been collected in pails and pans gave out. Men and women and children fainted from thirst and dropped in the streets.

When less than a day's supply of water was left, the townspeople came to Uzziah. They begged him to make peace with the Assyrians, as the other nations had done.

"Have courage, my brothers!" Uzziah answered them. "Let us hold out for five more days; by that time the Lord our God will restore to us his mercy, for he will not forsake us utterly. But if these days pass by, and no help comes for us, I will do what you say."

Sadly the women and children dragged themselves back to their homes. Slowly the men stumbled toward the towers and walls to guard them against the enemy. Everyone felt that death was near.

In Bethulia at this time there lived a wealthy widow named Judith. She was a very good woman. She was also very beautiful. When her maids told her what Uzziah had said to the people, Judith was much disturbed. She sent a maid to ask the rulers, Uzziah and Chabris and Charmis, to come to see her in her home.

These three rulers of Bethulia thought highly of Judith. Her husband had died three years before, leaving her much gold and silver and cattle and land. Judith had kept up the estate wisely and well. She lived simply in a small tent on the roof of her house, enjoying the rooms below only on sabbaths and feast days. She went on mourning for her husband and would not consider remarrying, though she was so beautiful and good and rich that many men would have liked her for a wife.

When the three rulers arrived, Judith spoke to them seriously. "What you have said to the people today is not right," she said, . . . "promising to surrender the city to our enemies unless the Lord turns and helps us within so many days. Who are you, that have put God to the test this day, and are setting yourselves up in the place of God? . . . If he does not choose to help us within these five days, he has the power to protect us within any time he pleases, or even to destroy us in the presence of our enemies."

Judith told the men that she felt sure God would save them, because she thought he would not want his people slain or taken captive, or his temple destroyed. And she reminded the rulers that the fate of all Judea and of the temple in Jerusalem depended on them in Bethulia. "Let us set an example to our brethren," she said to Uzziah and Chabris and Charmis.

Uzziah complimented Judith on her wisdom. "Pray for us," he begged her, "since you are a devout woman, and the Lord will send us rain to fill our cisterns and we will no longer be faint."

But Judith had a different idea. "Listen to me," she said. "I am about to do a thing which will go down through all generations of our descendants. Stand at the city gate tonight, and I will go out with my maid; and within the days after which you have promised to surrender the city to our enemies, the Lord will deliver Israel by my hand. Only, do not try to find out what I plan; for I will not tell you until I have finished what I am about to do."

All day Judith stayed in her tent and fasted and prayed. "Give to me, a widow, the strength to do what I plan," she begged God. "For thy power depends not upon numbers, nor thy might upon men of strength; for thou art God of the lowly, helper of the oppressed, upholder of the weak, protector of the forlorn, savior of those without hope."

Toward evening Judith went down into her house. She bathed herself, put on precious perfumes, combed her hair attractively, and dressed herself in her gayest, most becoming clothes. On her feet she put bright sandals and on her arms and ankles, glittering bracelets. Then she added rings and earrings. Finally she called her most trusted maid and gave her a bag of food and a bottle of wine to carry; and together they started for the town gate.

Uzziah and Chabris and Charmis were waiting there. They were amazed when they saw Judith dressed not in mourning but in gay clothes. They admired her beauty and said to her, "May the God of our fathers grant you favor and fulfil your plans, that the people of Israel may glory and Jerusalem may be exalted."

"Order the gate of the city to be opened for me," Judith directed, "and I will go out and accomplish the things about which you spoke with me."

The rulers ordered the gate to be opened. Then they stood and watched the two women go down the mountain path and on into the valley.

Judith headed straight for the Assyrian camp. Soon she met a patrol group of Holofernes' soldiers. When they questioned her, she told them that she was a Hebrew woman who wished to escape from Bethulia before the town was taken by the Assyrians. "I am on my way to the presence of Holofernes the commander of your army, to give him a true report," she said; "and I will show him a way by which he can go and capture all the hill country without losing one of his men, captured or slain."

The soldiers of the patrol listened, marveling at Judith's great beauty. When she finished speaking, they ordered men to escort her to the general. At Holofernes' tent the men left Judith outside while they went in to tell their general of the arrival of the lovely Hebrew woman. News of it spread through the camp and many soldiers came out of their tents and stood around Judith. "Who can despise these people, who have women like this among them?" they asked one another.

Finally the men led Judith into Holofernes' great tent. Holofernes had risen from his bed and had come to the front of the tent. The light from the silver lamps his men carried fell upon Judith, revealing her great beauty. She knelt before the general, but he directed his men to raise her up. "Take courage, woman," he said, "and do not be afraid in your heart, for I have never hurt any one who chose to serve Nebuchadnezzar, the king of all the earth. And even now, if your people who live in the hill country had not slighted me, I would never have lifted my spear against them; but they have brought all this on themselves. And now tell me why you have fled from them and have come over to us—since you have come to safety."

Judith answered Holofernes in a low, pleasant voice. First she praised his wisdom and goodness and his skill in military matters; then she spoke of Achior. She told Holofernes that the bound man had been taken into Bethulia where he had repeated to its leaders what he had said to the general. "My lord and master," said Judith, "do not disregard what he said, but keep it in your mind, for it is true: our nation cannot be punished, nor can the sword prevail against them, unless they sin against their God."

Then Judith stated, "And now . . . sin has overtaken them. . . . Since their food supply is exhausted and their water has almost given out, . . . they have decided to consume the first fruits of the grain and the tithes of wine and oil, which they had consecrated and set aside for the

47

priests. . . . Therefore, when I, your servant, learned all this, I fled from them."

Judith told Holofernes that through him God would punish the Hebrews for their sin, and that if he would allow her to remain in his camp, she would help him. But she must go out into the valley at night to pray, to learn from God when her people had touched the consecrated food. "Then," she promised, "I will lead you through the middle of Judea, till you come to Jerusalem; and I will set your throne in the midst of it."

Judith's words pleased Holofernes and his officers. "There is not such a woman from one end of the earth to the other, either for beauty of face or wisdom of speech!" they said. And Holofernes added, "God has done well to send you before the people, to lend strength to our hands and to bring destruction upon those who have slighted my lord. You are not only beautiful in appearance, but wise in speech; and if you do as you have said, your God shall be my God, and you shall live in the house of King Nebuchadnezzar and be renowned throughout the whole world."

The general commanded his men to set up a table in his tent and to serve Judith food on silver dishes. But Judith politely refused Holofernes' food. "I cannot eat it," she said, "lest it be an offense; but I will be provided from the things I have brought with me." In her bag, she explained, she had food that it was right for her to eat, according to the rules of her religion.

"If your supply runs out, where can we get more like it for you?" Holofernes asked.

Judith answered, "As your soul lives, my lord, your servant will not use up the things I have with me before the Lord carries out by my hand what he has determined to do."

After supper Holofernes' servants prepared a place for Judith and her maid to sleep. Toward morning they went out to pray, for Holofernes had ordered his guards to let the Hebrew woman and her maid do this and not to interfere with them in any way.

For three days Judith and her maid remained in Holofernes' camp. Each night they went out into the valley, where Judith bathed at a small spring and prayed to God.

On the fourth evening Holofernes gave a small dinner. He invited only a few of his slaves and Judith. Judith came dressed in her most becoming robe. As she reclined against the soft fleeces Holofernes had provided for her, the Assyrian general thought that he had never seen anyone so lovely.

"Drink now, and be merry with us!" he said to her.

"I will drink now, my lord," Judith answered, "because my life means more to me today than in all the days since I was born." But she drank the wine her maid had brought, not Holofernes' wine.

Holofernes was so dazzled by Judith's beauty and so entranced by her charm that he drank much more wine than he had ever before drunk at one time. The dinner went on and on until at last all the weary guests left, all except Judith. By this time Holofernes was quite overcome with wine, and he stretched himself out on his bed.

Judith's maid was waiting outside the tent for her, ready to go into the valley as usual. No one except Judith was inside the tent with the general. The time had come! The beautiful woman moved toward Holofernes' bed. Silently she stood beside it and prayed to God. Noiselessly she took down the great sword which hung above the bed. "Give me strength this day, O Lord God of Israel!" she prayed. She grasped the hair of the general's head and struck his neck twice with all her might. Then she tumbled Holofernes' headless body off the bed and pulled down the handsome canopy that had been over the bed.

At the door of the tent Judith thrust Holofernes' head into the food bag held by her startled maid. She herself carried the canopy she had torn down. The two women started for the spring in the valley, as they had done each night. And the guards let them go, as they had been ordered to do.

But this night Judith and her maid did not stop at the spring. They circled around the valley and went up a hidden mountain path that led to Bethulia. When they came near the town gate, Judith cried to the watchman, "Open, open the gate! God, our God, is still with us, to show his power in Israel, and his strength against our enemies, even as he has done this day!"

The men at the gate recognized Judith's voice. Excitedly they spread the word that she had returned. In spite of their weakness the townspeople hurried to greet her. They hardly dared believe that Judith was safely back or that there was good news for them. Quickly they built a fire to light the dark night, then gathered around to listen to the brave woman's story.

Judith opened her bag. "See," she said, "here is the head of Holofernes, the commander of the Assyrian army, and here is the canopy beneath which he lay in his drunken stupor." She spread out the handsome, gem-encrusted canopy. "The Lord has struck him down by the hand of a woman," Judith said proudly.

The astonished people shouted for joy, then knelt down and worshiped God. Uzziah praised Judith and asked the blessings of God upon her. Achior, the Ammonite, almost fainted with surprise when he saw the head. Then he, too, praised Judith, and he accepted the Hebrew God as his God.

Judith now directed the men what to do next. At dawn every man and boy who could carry a weapon was to arm himself. They should go out of the gates and line up on the hillside in battle formation, within sight of the Assyrian outposts. When the soldiers saw them, they would run to tell their officers that the foolish mountain people had come out to battle against the great army of Nebuchadnezzar. And then, said Judith, the Assyrians would discover what had taken place in Holofernes' tent.

And so it happened. At dawn the Hebrew men armed themselves and lined up on the hillside. The Assyrian outposts ran to call their officers. And then a great cry went up from the Assyrian camp: "The slaves have tricked us! One Hebrew woman has brought disgrace upon the house of King Nebuchadnezzar! For look, here is Holofernes lying on the ground, and his head is not on him!"

The shouts and cries of the Assyrian officers awakened the soldiers in the tents. And when they heard what had happened, they were so overcome with terror and fear that they fled across the plain by any path they could find. The men of Bethulia and nearby towns ran after them and destroyed many of them.

The joyful people of Bethulia stumbled down the mountainside and into the Assyrian camp. On the way they drank from the springs, and in the camp they ate from the plentiful supply of food. Then they plundered the officers' tents of their riches. They took to Judith the silver dishes and the fine furnishings they found in Holofernes' tent. There was so much in the camp that there was still plenty left for the men when they returned after destroying the enemy.

Messengers carried word of the victory to Jerusalem. The high priest and the men of the senate made the journey to Bethulia to see the place where God had done this great thing for Israel and to thank Judith. "You are the exaltation of Jerusalem, you are the great glory of Israel, you are the great pride of our nation!" they said to her. "May the Almighty Lord bless you for ever!" And the proud and happy people of Bethulia shouted, "So be it!"

Women crowned themselves with olive wreaths and danced in Judith's honor. Then, to celebrate the victory, Judith herself led the women in the dance and the men marched behind them, bearing weapons and wearing garlands of flowers. They formed a procession and marched about the town, singing. And Judith led them in a hymn of thanksgiving which started:

> "Begin a song to my God with tambourines,
>     sing to my Lord with cymbals.
> Raise to him a new psalm;
>     exalt him, and call upon his name."

The song told the story of Judith's daring deed, then went on:

> "I will sing to my God a new song:
> O Lord, thou art great and glorious,
>     wonderful in strength, invincible."

The people of Bethulia made the long journey down to Jerusalem to give thanks to God in the temple, and Judith went with them. She took the treasures from Holofernes' tent to present to the temple. The Bethulians stayed in the holy city for three months, making their offerings in the temple, and feasting and praising God.

When they returned to Bethulia, Judith stayed quietly on her estate. Many men wanted to marry her, but she remained a widow. She set free the maid who had gone with her to the Assyrian camp. Judith was honored throughout the whole country of Judea. Every year her name became more renowned.

"And no one ever again spread terror among the people of Israel in the days of Judith, or for a long time after her death."

## QUEEN ESTHER GOES BEFORE THE KING

Almost everyone knows the Old Testament story of beautiful Queen Esther. They admire her for her courage in telling her husband, the king of Persia, that the Jewish people were her people and for pleading with him to spare their lives. Each year Esther's brave deed is celebrated by the Jews in the festival of *Purim,* or *Hadassah.* In the Apocrypha there are several additions to the popular story of Esther. These belong in various places in the tale. When they are separated from the Book of Esther and set down together, they do not make a complete story, but they provide additional details which add interest to the original story.

55

The first Apocrypha addition is a dream of Mordecai, Esther's cousin and guardian. He dreamed of two fighting dragons and of nations preparing to battle against "the nation of the righteous." But when the people of the righteous nation cried to God, he heard them and "as though from a tiny spring, there came a great river, with abundant water; light came, and the sun rose, and the lowly were exalted and consumed those held in honor."

When Mordecai awoke, he kept thinking about his dream and trying to understand its meaning. As he rested in a court he overheard a plot against the king, which he reported. The two guilty men were punished, and Mordecai was rewarded. This angered Haman, a friend of the guilty men and a great favorite of the king, so much that he swore to destroy Mordecai and Mordecai's people, the Jews.

Haman managed to get the king's permission to send out a letter, bearing the royal seal, to the rulers of all the provinces in the kingdom. The letter named a day, not far off, on which every Jew in every province should be slain. The second Apocrypha addition to Esther gives the contents of this letter.

The Apocrypha gives the prayer of Mordecai after he heard the dreadful news. He begged God to save the people of Israel and prayed: "Turn our mourning into feasting, that we may live and sing praise to thy name, O Lord."

The Apocrypha also gives the prayer of Esther, the

young queen, after she had promised Mordecai to try to save her people. The king, she knew, had no idea that his queen was a Jewess or that she was related to Mordecai. Although it was against the law to approach the king without permission, Esther agreed to enter the throne room, uninvited, to try to speak to the king.

Esther, the Apocrypha tells us, "put on the garments of distress and mourning." She fasted and prayed to God: "Give me courage, O King of the gods and Master of all dominion! Put eloquent speech in my mouth before the lion. . . . Save us by thy hand, and help me, who am alone and have no helper but thee, O Lord. . . . And save me from my fear!"

The Apocrypha then gives details about Esther's appearance and her coming before the king.

Beautifully dressed in her royal robes and adorned with her precious jewels, Esther timidly prepared to enter the presence of the king with her two maids. The queen walked slowly and proudly into the throne room, "leaning daintily on one, while the other followed carrying her train. She was radiant with perfect beauty, and she looked happy, as if beloved, but her heart was frozen with fear."

The king saw Esther coming uninvited before the royal throne and "he looked at her in fierce anger. And the queen faltered, and turned pale and faint, and collapsed upon the head of the maid who went before her."

Then the king's love for Esther overcame his anger. "God changed the spirit of the king to gentleness, and in alarm he sprang from his throne and took her in his arms until she came to herself. And he comforted her with soothing words." Touching the queen with his golden scepter, he bade her speak.

The Old Testament story relates the clever way Esther informed the king of Haman's plot against the Jews. It tells how the king ordered Haman's death and gave his place to Mordecai.

The Apocrypha adds the letter which the king allowed Mordecai to send out in his name. This letter informed the rulers of the provinces that Haman had been hanged because he deceived the king and plotted against the Jews. It advised them not to carry out the orders in Haman's letter but rather to help the Jews. And the letter suggested that the rulers turn the day Haman had set for the Jews' destruction from a time of death into a time of joy.

Only after all of this, according to the Apocrypha, did Mordecai understand the meaning of the dream which had puzzled him. Then he knew that the tiny spring which became a river was Esther; that the fighting dragons were Haman and himself; and that the nation that cried out to God and was saved, was Israel.

## SUSANNA AND THE TWO EVIL ELDERS

In nearly every one of the great art galleries of Europe
there is a picture, often by a master painter, that puzzles
some Americans. Usually it shows two old men peering out
from behind bushes at a beautiful woman who is bathing in
a pool or fountain. If a curious American asks the guide
about it, he explains, "It is a picture of the Bible story of
Susanna." That leaves the American more puzzled than
ever, for he is sure he has never read that story in his Bible.
Nor has he, if he reads a Protestant Bible, for it is in the
Apocrypha. But very likely the European guide would find
the story in his Bible, in the book of Daniel. It is a part of
that book in the Catholic Bible.

59

In the days when the Jews were captive in Babylon there lived in that city a Jew named Joachim. He was a wealthy man and a good one. All the Hebrews of Babylon looked up to him and to his wife, Susanna. Susanna was a very beautiful woman, and she was as good as she was beautiful.

Joachim and Susanna and their family lived in a large house surrounded by lovely gardens. It was such a big place that Joachim had invited the court which ruled over the affairs of the Jews to hold its meetings there. Every morning people came to Joachim's house to have their disputes settled by the Hebrew judges. At noon, after the people had left, Susanna would go with her maids into the gardens. There she would walk about, enjoying the fragrant flowers, the green shade of the trees, and the coolness of the fountains and pools.

One year two elderly men were appointed judges of the Hebrew court. Every morning they came to Joachim's house to settle the people's disputes. When they left at noon, they often saw Susanna coming out of the house to walk in the gardens.

These two elderly judges were not so good as they should have been. Each of them began to look longingly at the beautiful Susanna. Each of them wished she were not Joachim's wife so that she might belong to him. Day after day the two elders hurried through the work of the court. Often their heads were so full of thoughts of Susanna that they did not pay much attention to what they were doing. Every afternoon they lingered on after the people were gone, hoping to catch a glimpse of Joachim's lovely wife.

One noon one elder said to the other, "Let us go home, for it is mealtime." They walked out of the garden together and at the gate they parted, each headed for his own home. But the minute they were out of sight of one another, both of them turned back. At the garden gate they met. They hemmed and hawed and stuttered and stammered, unable to think of a good excuse for their return. At last they confessed to each other that they had come back to feast their eyes on Susanna.

Then the two evil old men put their heads together to try to figure out a way to find Susanna alone, without her maids. They decided to hide in the gardens every noon to watch for her.

One day as the two elders crouched behind some bushes, Susanna came out as usual with her two maids. It was a very hot day, and Susanna decided to cool herself off by bathing in one of the garden pools. She asked the maids to go back to the house to get oils and ointments, and to shut the garden doors so that no one could come in.

The minute the maids had left, the two evil old men ran out from behind the bushes. "Look," they whispered to Susanna, "the garden doors are shut, no one sees us, and we are in love with you." And they begged her to let them make love to her. "If you refuse," they threatened, "we will testify against you that a young man was with you, and this was why you sent your maids away."

Susanna saw that she was trapped. She knew that the punishment for unfaithfulness to a husband was death. She also knew that the word of these two judges would be believed above hers. But she did not hesitate. "I choose not to do it and to fall into your hands, rather than to sin in the sight of the Lord," she said. And then she called for help.

The two elders called, too, and one of them ran and opened the garden doors.

The servants in the house heard the shouts and rushed out to the garden. The two judges told the story they had made up—that they had found Susanna with a young man. This surprised the servants and made them feel very much ashamed. Never before had anyone ever breathed a word against their mistress.

The next morning the two judges sent for Susanna to appear before the court. She came, heavily veiled. With her were her parents, who were righteous people, and her children and her brothers and sisters. The two judges, wanting to enjoy Susanna's beauty, ordered her to take off her veil. She did this, and stood there looking so lovely and pitiable that her family wept. Susanna wept, too, and she looked upward, "for her heart trusted in the Lord."

Then the two evil judges told their false story. "As we were walking in the garden alone," they said, "this woman came in with her two maids, shut the garden doors, and dismissed the maids. Then a young man, who had been hidden, came to her." The old men went on to say that when they saw the two embrace, they ran toward them and tried to seize the young man. "But," they concluded, "he was too strong for us, and he opened the doors and dashed out."

Because they were judges, their story was believed; and Susanna was condemned to death. She prayed aloud to God, declaring her innocence before him, but the people did not listen.

As Susanna was being led away to her death, a young man named Daniel cried out and made the people stop. "Have you condemned a daughter of Israel without examination and without learning the facts?" he asked. "Return to the place of judgment. For these men have borne false witness against her."

The people hurried back, and Daniel was invited to speak. He asked for the privilege of examining the two witnesses separately.

When only one of the judges stood before him, Daniel accused him, saying, "Your sins have now come home, which you have committed in the past, pronouncing unjust judgments, condemning the innocent, and letting the guilty go free." Finally Daniel asked the old judge one question: "Now then, if you really saw her, tell me this: Under what tree did you see them?"

The old judge answered, "Under a mastic tree."

Then Daniel asked the people to take the first elder

63

aside and bring the other one to him. Daniel accused this judge, too, of past wickedness. And then he asked him the same question he had asked the first judge: "Under what tree did you catch them?"

The second old judge answered, "Under an evergreen oak."

At this everyone shouted and praised God, because they saw that God had saved the one who had trusted in him. Out of their own mouths the witnesses had proved that their story was false. And instead of Susanna, the two evil judges who had wickedly lied about her were put to death.

Susanna's parents and her husband and all her family praised God for Susanna, because she had resisted evil and had not done wrong.

As for the young man Daniel, from that day on he was honored by the people for his great wisdom.

## DANIEL AND BEL

"The history of the destruction of Bel and the Dragon,"
says the King James Version of the Apocrypha, was "cut off
from the end of Daniel." The first of these two short stories,
the story about Bel, is one of the oldest detective stories in
the world, and one of the best.

Daniel, one of the Jewish captives in Babylon, was
treated very well there. He was so wise and clever and
faithful that he became an important man in the king's
palace. In fact, he became an honored friend of the king
himself. But there was one thing which Daniel refused to

65

do. He would not go with the king to worship the great idol Bel.

Bel was the most popular idol in Babylon. The king and the people of Babylon thought so much of this god that they kept him supplied with plenty to eat and drink. Every day they gave Bel twelve bushels of fine flour, forty sheep, and fifty gallons of wine.

The king was annoyed that Daniel would not worship Bel. When he asked Daniel for his reason, Daniel replied, "Because I do not revere man-made idols, but the living God, who created heaven and earth."

"Do you not think that Bel is a living God?" the king asked. "Do you not see how much he eats and drinks every day?"

At that, Daniel laughed. "Do not be deceived, O king," said Daniel; "for this is but clay inside and brass outside, and it never ate or drank anything."

This made the king very angry. He called in the seventy priests who served in the great temple of Bel. "If you do not tell me who is eating these provisions," he said, "you shall die. But if you prove that Bel is eating them, Daniel shall die."

The priests did not seem worried. They suggested a way to prove that Bel really ate the food put before him. They said that they would all go out of the temple and the king himself could place the food and wine before Bel, then shut the door and seal it with his great seal. "And when you return in the morning," they said, "if you do not find that Bel has eaten it all, we will die; or else Daniel will, who is telling lies about us."

The priests felt that they were safe with this plan, for there was a hidden door beneath the table on which Bel's food and wine were placed. Every night the priests and their wives and children went in through the secret door and ate the idol's food and drank the wine.

The king approved the priests' plan. When they left, he set out the food and wine for Bel. Then he watched while, at Daniel's suggestion, servants sprinkled fine ashes over the temple floor. After this had been done, everyone went out, and the great door of the temple was shut and sealed with the king's seal.

That night the priests and their wives and children went into the temple by the secret door as usual. They ate every crumb of the idol's food and drank every drop of the wine.

Early the next morning the king took Daniel with him to the temple of Bel.

"Are the seals unbroken, Daniel?" the king asked.

"They are unbroken, O king," answered Daniel.

Then the king ordered the seals to be broken and the door opened. Eagerly he looked at the table before Bel. Not a morsel of food was there, not a drop of wine. In a loud voice the king shouted, "You are great, O Bel; and with you there is no deceit, none at all."

But Daniel laughed. "Look at the floor, and notice whose footsteps these are," he said to the king.

The king looked down. In the fine ashes the servants had spread over the floor he saw the marks of many feet. Astonished, he said, "I see the footsteps of men and women and children."

Then the king's amazement turned to anger. He sent for the priests and forced them to show him the secret door. And then, as he had vowed, he had them put to death. Bel, and the temple of Bel, he gave over to Daniel. And Daniel destroyed them both.

## DANIEL AND THE DRAGON

This second story "cut off from the end of Daniel" is one of the strangest stories in the Apocrypha. It tells of a clever trick, a startling journey, and a miraculous escape.

Besides worshiping Bel, the people of Babylon also worshiped a great serpent, or dragon. "You cannot deny that this is a living god; so worship him," the king said to Daniel.

But Daniel refused. "I will worship the Lord my God, for he is the living God," he told the king.

Daniel knew that the king believed the dragon would live forever and that no one could harm him. To show the king how foolish this idea was, Daniel asked permission to try to slay the dragon without either a sword or a club. The king smiled. "I give you permission," he said.

Daniel boiled together some pitch, some fat, and some hair. He made the sticky mixture up into little cakes and fed them to the dragon. The greedy dragon ate the cakes. And soon he burst open!

"See what you have been worshiping!" Daniel said to the king.

The king grew thoughtful, but when the people of Babylon heard that the sacred dragon was dead they became very angry. They were angry with Daniel, who had fed the dragon the cakes which had killed him. They were also angry with the king, who had ordered the priests of Bel slain and who had let Daniel destroy first Bel and his temple and then the dragon.

"Hand Daniel over to us, or else we will kill you and your household," they shouted to the king.

The king saw that he had no choice. So, much as he hated to do it, he handed Daniel over to the mob.

The angry people threw Daniel into the lion's den. Seven lions were kept in this den, and each day they were fed much meat. On this day, however, the people did not give the lions any meat at all. Now, they thought, the beasts will surely leap upon Daniel and devour him.

But the lions did not leap upon Daniel. They did not

even touch him. For six days he sat safely in the midst of the lions. All this time, he had nothing to eat and he became very hungry.

In faraway Judea the prophet Habakkuk was starting out from his house. In his hand was a bowl of bread and soup he was taking to the reapers in the field. Suddenly he heard an angel's voice saying, "Take the dinner which you have to Babylon, to Daniel, in the lions' den."

Habakkuk was bewildered. "Sir," he said to the angel, "I have never seen Babylon, and I know nothing about the den."

Then the angel took Habakkuk by the top of his head and, holding him by the hair, carried him with the speed of the wind to Babylon. There he set the prophet down by the lions' den.

"Daniel! Daniel!" shouted Habakkuk. "Take the dinner which God has sent you."

Daniel thanked God, then rose and ate. And the angel took Habakkuk back to Judea.

On the seventh day the king came to the lions' den to mourn for Daniel. Sadly he looked in. And there he saw Daniel, sitting in the midst of the lions, safe and sound. "Thou art great, O Lord God of Daniel," the king cried out, "and there is no other besides thee." And he pulled Daniel out of the lions' den and threw into it the men who had tried to kill him.

## IN THE FIERY FURNACE

This is the third of the three books in the Apocrypha which were written as additions to the Old Testament book of Daniel. The other two are Susanna, and Bel and the Dragon.

Although the book of Daniel is set in the days of the captivity of the Hebrews in Babylonia, it was probably written much later, in another time of trouble. The Jewish people in this later time could well appreciate the wonderful spirit of the three young men in this story who were true to their religion.

This splendid psalm of praise and thanksgiving, a little

like psalms 136 and 148, has been used in Christian church services for many centuries. It is called the *Benedicite*.

Daniel's three Hebrew friends, Shadrach, Meshach, and Abednego, refused to obey an order of the king, Nebuchadnezzar. The order was to bow down and worship the great golden statue which King Nebuchadnezzar had set up near the city of Babylon. They were given their choice: worship the golden statue or be thrown into a burning fiery furnace. When the three young men continued to refuse to worship the statue, Nebuchadnezzar grew very angry. He ordered the furnace to be heated seven times hotter than usual, and then the three men were bound and thrown into it. This is told in the third chapter of the Old Testament book of Daniel.

Now the Apocrypha story begins. The three young men walked around in the midst of the flames, singing hymns to God and blessing him. Then Azariah (Abednego's true Hebrew name) prayed to God. He prayed that their lives might be accepted as an offering to the Lord, and he asked God to break the strength of those who harmed his followers. "Let them know that thou art the Lord, the only God, glorious over the whole world," he prayed.

The king's servants added more and more fuel to the fire. They threw in naphtha and pitch and tow and brush to make it burn more fiercely. The flames leaped up high above the furnace. They streamed out from it, burning the people who came too close.

But an angel of God came into the furnace to be with the three young men. And he drove the fiery flames out of the furnace, and made the inside of the furnace like a moist wind. The fire did not touch the three young men at all or hurt or trouble them in any way.

The three young men, as with one voice, broke into a song of praise and thanksgiving to God. There in the midst of the fiery furnace they sang verse after verse after verse, asking all things in heaven and all things on earth to bless God. They asked sun and moon, the stars of heaven, rain and dew, winter cold and summer heat, light and darkness, mountains and hills, springs, seas, and rivers, birds of the air, beasts and cattle to "sing praise to him and highly exalt him for ever." They also asked the sons of men, the people of Israel, and the priests of the Lord to "sing praise to him and highly exalt him for ever."

Finally Shadrach, Meshach, and Abednego (Azariah) thanked God for saving them from death in the burning fiery furnace. They ended their great song of praise:

"Give thanks to the Lord, for he is good,
    for his mercy endures for ever.
Bless him, all who worship the Lord,
    the God of gods,
      sing praise to him and give thanks to him,
    for his mercy endures for ever."

## THE STORY OF A BRAVE FAMILY

The Jews who returned to Palestine after the captivity in Babylonia were under the rule of the Persian Empire. This great empire included most of the land east of the Mediterranean Sea. It existed for about two hundred years, from about five hundred to three hundred years before the birth of Christ. The kings who ruled over this empire did not interfere too much with the Jews, but let them live and worship God according to their ancient customs.

Then, about three centuries before Christ, Alexander the Great of Macedonia, the country just north of Greece, set out to conquer the world. He took over one land after another—Greece, Egypt, Mesopotamia, Assyria, Babylonia, and all the countries in between, including Palestine. After Alexander's death his great kingdom was split up. The rulers who controlled Palestine made the Jews pay heavy taxes; but they, too, let the people go on living and worshiping in their own way.

It was not until nearly two hundred years before Christ that the Jews had any real trouble. Then the Syrian king Antiochus Epiphanes became ruler of the lands east of the Mediterranean. Antiochus felt that the Greek way of life was best, and he decided to put an end to all religions and customs that were not Greek. Most of the Jews, however, were determined to hold fast to their own ways, and especially to their belief in one God and their manner of worshiping him.

The last two books of the Apocrypha, the First and Second Books of the Maccabees, tell the heroic story of this band of faithful Jews fighting for their right to this belief.


The kingdom of Antiochus Ephiphanes stretched eastward from the Mediterranean for hundreds and hundreds of miles. It was made up of many countries and many different peoples. When Antiochus decreed that all should live as the Greeks lived, the peoples in most of the countries did not mind. Even some of the Jews in the land of Palestine did not object. They gave up their old Hebrew customs. They ate foods that were forbidden to Jews. They built a gymnasium in Jerusalem where young men played Greek games. A few Jews even began to worship

Greek gods. But there were other Jews, many of them, who would not do these things. These Jews were determined to be true to their God. They swore to live as the law of Moses taught them to live, whatever the cost.

Antiochus knew how the Jews felt. He came down to their great city of Jerusalem with a large army. Entering their temple he carried away the precious things dedicated to the service of God. He took the sacred gold altar and the golden lampstand and candlesticks and bowls, the beautiful altar table, and the fine draperies. He even stripped the gold and silver decorations from the front of the temple. All these treasures he carried away to Syria, leaving the Jews angry and heartbroken at this plundering. But there was nothing they could do about it.

Two years later Antiochus sent a collector of tribute to Jerusalem. This man pretended to be friendly at first; but he came with a large force, and suddenly he destroyed most of the city and took many of the Jews away as slaves. He built a great fortress there for his soldiers, and he decreed that all Jews left in Palestine must follow the Greek ways or die.

The soldiers of Antiochus knew very well that the Jews considered swine unclean animals. They would not eat these animals or sacrifice them on their altars. But Antiochus' soldiers made the Jews eat swine and other Gentile, or non-Jewish, foods. They forced them to celebrate the Greek feasts and worship Greek gods at Greek altars and sacrifice swine to them there.

77

Many Jews did these things in order to save their lives. Others left their homes and fled to foreign countries. Still others moved into small villages in the countryside, where they thought Antiochus' soldiers would not bother them. Some even went into hiding in caves in the desert. And very many Jews died rather than give up their religion.

Among those who moved out of Jerusalem to escape Antiochus' soldiers was an old priest named Mattathias. He settled with his family of five sons in the little town of Modein, twenty miles or so from Jerusalem. There he hoped he and his family could quietly go on worshiping God as they had always done.

But one day the foreign soldiers came to Modein to carry out Antiochus' commands. Their chief officer saw how highly the people thought of Mattathias, the old priest; so the officer spoke first to him. "You are a leader, honored and great in this city, and supported by sons and brothers," the officer said. "Now be the first to come and do what the king commands, as all the Gentiles and the men of Judah and those that are left in Jerusalem have done. Then you and your sons will be numbered among the friends of the king, and you and your sons will be honored with silver and gold and many gifts."

Old Mattathias did not mince his words when he replied. Loudly and boldly he declared: "Even if all the nations that live under the rule of the king obey him, and have chosen to do his commandments, departing each one from the religion of his fathers, yet I and my sons and my brothers will live by the covenant of our fathers. . . . We will not obey the king's words."

As Mattathias finished speaking, another Jew stepped up to the altar to do what Mattathias would not do. This filled the old priest with righteous anger. He lifted his hand and killed both the Jew who was about to make the forbidden sacrifice and the king's officer. Then Mattathias tore down the heathen altar. Turning to the men of Modein, he cried: "Let every one who is zealous for the law and supports the covenant come out with me!" And with his five sons the old priest fled to the hills of the desert. Many Jews joined him there, bringing along their families and their cattle.

The king's troops in the Jerusalem fortress heard of Mattathias' rebellion. They marched out into the hill country to punish the rebels, and found some of them in their caves. It was the sabbath, and the rebels did not try to defend themselves, because it was against the Jews' religion to fight on the sabbath. The king's soldiers struck out with their swords to right and left, killing the Jews without mercy.

When Mattathias heard of this slaughter, he was sick at heart. He was not only sad for his slain comrades, but he was concerned for the future. The enemy, he felt, was sure to return on another sabbath to find and kill them all. This, he decided, must not happen. If all the faithful Jews died, their religion would die, too. They must live, to keep the true religion alive in the world!

Mattathias spoke to his followers, who agreed with him. And so it was decided that if the king's soldiers ever attacked on the sabbath again, the Jews would fight back.

The king's soldiers did return; they returned many times. They came on the sabbath day and on other days. Every time Mattathias' men fought bravely for their people and their religion. And every time they were able to hold off the enemy.

Mattathias, himself, was a very old man. A year or so after the retreat to the hills and the start of the rebellion, he died. Then his son Simon became the rebels' counselor; and a younger son, Judas, became their commander. All those who had stood by Mattathias now fought under Judas, who was also called Maccabeus—the hammerer.

Judas Maccabeus had great military ability. He also had a strong faith in God. "It is not on the size of the army that victory in battle depends," Judas told his men, "but strength comes from Heaven. . . . We fight for our lives and our laws." And he led his courageous men against the foreign soldiers in Judah and won many victories.

King Antiochus, in his palace in Antioch in Syria, was surprised and angry at the victories of the Jews over his soldiers. He was about to go to Persia, but before he left he ordered his governor, Lysias, to correct the situation in Palestine. Lysias, the king said, should wipe out the troublesome people of Judah completely and settle new people there; and to do the job, Antiochus turned over to his governor half of his troops and his war elephants.

Lysias chose three of his best generals to lead the Syrian army south to Judah. They camped on the plain below the hills where the rebels were. When Judas saw the army, he knew that the Jews would have to fight a great battle. He ordered his men to fast and to pray to God for help. Then he had the trumpets blown. He divided his men into companies and appointed their captains. "Gird yourselves and be valiant," Judas told them. "Be ready early in the morning to fight with these Gentiles who have assembled against us to destroy us and our sanctuary."

One of the Syrian generals decided to lead a company of men in a surprise night attack on the Jewish camp. Judas heard of the plan, and he led his men quietly out of the camp. When the Syrian soldiers arrived, they did not find anyone there. Thinking the Jews had fled into the hills, the Syrian soldiers went after them.

But Judas' men had not gone into the hills. Instead, Judas had led them around to the back of the Syrian camp. At daybreak he and his men crashed in upon the Syrian soldiers left there. Surprised and confused, they fled. Judas' men ran after them, killing many. Then they returned and drew themselves up in battle formation, ready to meet the company which had gone out at night.

When these soldiers came back, weary from their useless search in the hills, they found their army gone and the Jews waiting for them. Then they, too, fled, and they kept on going until they were out of the Jews' country.

Judas and his men found rich treasure in the enemy camp. There were supplies and equipment which they needed badly. Marching back to their hill caves loaded down with their spoils they sang hymns of praise to God for their victory.

When Lysias heard of his army's defeat, he was dismayed. The next year he sent a much larger army into Judah. Judas and his brave men defeated this army, too. After this second great victory, Judas decided that he and his men could leave the desert hill country and go back to Jerusalem.

In Jerusalem the Jewish rebels wept when they saw the desolation of their beloved temple on Mount Zion. Its walls were torn down; bushes grew in the courts; and the sacred altar was no longer holy, for it had been used by the foreigners.

Judas' men set to work at once to cleanse and repair the temple. They tore down the altar and built a new one. They repaired the walls and cleaned up the courts. They hung new curtains and made new holy vessels. Then they burned incense on the new altar and lighted the lamps.

Exactly three years after the foreigners had taken over the temple, the Jews rededicated it "with songs and harps and lutes and cymbals. . . . They celebrated the dedication of the altar for eight days. . . . There was very great gladness among the people, and the reproach of the Gentiles was removed."

From that time on, the Jews decided, "every year at that season the days of the dedication of the altar should be observed with gladness and joy for eight days." This was the beginning of the festival of lights or of dedication, called *Hannukah,* or *Chanukah.*

It annoyed the Gentile nations around Judah that the Jews were becoming so independent and successful. But when these warlike neighbors made trouble for the Jews, Judas and his men met them in battle and defeated them. And when Jews in other parts of Palestine had trouble with outsiders, the Maccabee brothers went to their rescue. They helped the people in Galilee in the north and in Gilead across the Jordan. Many of the Jews from these two regions went back with their rescuers to Judah. Some of them joined the rebel army, which grew stronger and stronger. And all praised its leader, Judas Maccabeus.

The Syrians still in Judah were continually trying to defeat Judas. To prevent this, Judas tried to capture the Syrian soldiers' fortress in Jerusalem. When it seemed as if he would succeed, the soldiers in the fortress sent to Antioch for help, and before long Lysias set out with a third great army against the Jewish rebels. Thousands of Syrian horsemen and tens of thousands of Syrian soldiers on foot marched south into Palestine. With them were thirty-two war elephants. Before a battle each elephant had a covered wooden tower harnessed to his back. In the tower were four spearsmen who were trained to shoot down on the enemy soldiers.

The two armies met on a great plain. The Jews, though they had never seen such an army, advanced bravely and fought with courage. Eleazar, a younger brother of Judas Maccabeus, saw the royal armor on one huge elephant and fought his way toward it. He reached it, and stabbed the great beast from beneath. The elephant came crashing down, and in its fall it crushed Eleazar to death. He was the first of Mattathias' five sons to die.

The Syrian army was so powerful that at last Judas ordered the Jews to retreat into the hills. Lysias' soldiers did not follow them there. Instead, they went up to Jerusalem and laid siege to Mount Zion, where the temple stood. It was enclosed by strong walls, which Judas had built. Soldiers were there to defend it, but they were not prepared for a siege. They would have had a hard time if Lysias had not decided that he must return quickly to Antioch to save that city from an invading army. He was so anxious to go that he agreed not to disturb Mount Zion, and to let the Jews live by their own laws. After he left, however, Syrian soldiers disregarded Lysias' promises and tore down the walls on Mount Zion.

Later, Judas fought another great battle against the Syrian army led by a brilliant general named Nicanor. This time Judas was successful. After this battle the Jews had a rest from fighting for a while.

For some time Judas had been hearing much about the Romans. They were becoming a more and more important power in the world. Judas knew that they had conquered many countries, both far and near, and had made alliances with some of them. He heard that the Romans kept their word with these countries. He was told: "With their friends and those who rely on them, they have kept friendship." Judas also knew about the senate in Rome and its good government of the people.

So Judas sent two trusted men from Jerusalem to ask the Roman senate for a Jewish alliance. The senate agreed. It accepted the Jews as allies and made a treaty of peace with them. And it sent word to the Syrian king: "Why have you made your yoke heavy upon our friends and allies the Jews? If now they appeal again for help against you, we will defend their rights and fight you on sea and on land."

But before this letter arrived in Antioch, the Syrian army had gone again into Palestine. It was a huge army, much larger than Judas' army. The religious warriors who had stood beside Judas while he was fighting to save their religion had left him because they believed he was thinking too much about national matters. They did not care whether Judah was an independent country or not. All they wanted was freedom to worship God in the way they believed to be right.

With the religious warriors gone, Judas had only about eight hundred men in his army, and these seemed to have lost some of their courage. They begged Judas not to fight until he had more soldiers. But Judas would not listen. "Far be it from us to do such a thing as to flee from them,"

85

he said. "If our time has come, let us die bravely for our brethren, and leave no cause to question our honor."

So Judas led his men into battle against the Syrians. The Jews fought bravely, but they lost the battle, and Judas was killed. All Judah mourned for Judas Maccabeus, the mighty warrior.

There were bad times in Judah after Judas' death. The Jews who did not care deeply about their religion flocked over to the enemy. Jonathan, Judas' youngest brother, became the Jews' leader. For a time he had to stay in the desert country beyond the Jordan River, because the Syrian general was trying to capture him. When the general finally gave up and went back to Syria, Jonathan returned to Jerusalem. He rebuilt the walls around the temple. Once more Jerusalem became a city of Jews faithful to the One God and the laws of Moses. But the strong foreign fortress still stood there, a constant annoyance to them all.

Jonathan became the Jews' high priest as well as their commander and governor. Under his rule the country prospered and the army again became large. He sent men to Rome to renew the treaty of friendship made by Judas. On their way back, the men stopped at the Greek city of Sparta to assure the Spartans of the Jews' friendship. Both in Rome and in Sparta the Jewish representatives were received courteously and given messages of friendship to take back to Jerusalem.

With these promises, the future of Jonathan as ruler of the Jews seemed secure. But an ambitious Syrian military man named Trypho decided to try to seize the throne of Syria and to become king of all Asia. Certain that Jonathan would oppose such a scheme, Trypho determined to get rid of the Jewish leader. At first he intended to make war against the Jews, but when he saw how strong the Jewish army was he gave up that idea. Instead, he managed to persuade Jonathan to go into a Syrian city for a peace conference. Once Jonathan was inside, Trypho had the gates of the city locked, and Jonathan became his prisoner.

The people of Israel were sad when they heard of Jonathan's capture. They were fearful, too, because they felt sure, now that they were without a leader, Trypho and the unfriendly nations around them would try to destroy Judah.

Simon, the oldest of Mattathias' five sons, gathered the people around him. He reminded them that his father and all his brothers had given their lives to their country. "And now," said Simon, "far be it from me to spare my life in any time of distress, for I am not better than my brothers."

The people gladly made Simon their leader. "Fight our battles," they said, "and all that you say to us we will do."

When Trypho heard that Simon was taking Jonathan's place, he sent word to him that his brother was safe and was only being held for the money he owed the royal treasury. If the Jews would send the money, he would release Jonathan at once.

Simon knew very well that he could not trust Trypho's words. But he and his people wanted to do everything possible to win Jonathan's release, so they sent the money. As Simon expected, Trypho broke his word and killed Jonathan.

Simon proved to be a wonderful leader of the people of Israel. Trypho did not dare invade the country. Simon fortified Jerusalem on every side. He starved out the Syrian garrison in their fortress in Jerusalem and put Jewish soldiers in it. He strengthened the towns all over Judah, and captured for the Jews a foreign city and a harbor on the Mediterranean. He also renewed the treaties of friendship with Rome and with Sparta.

A long Hebrew poem tells of Simon's deeds.

"He established peace in the land,
    and Israel rejoiced with great joy.
Each man sat under his vine and his fig tree,
    and there was none to make them afraid."

The Jewish people made Simon their high priest and commander and protector. They decreed "that he should be obeyed by all, and that all contracts in the country should be written in his name, and that he should be clothed in purple and wear gold."

For many years the Jewish people were peaceful and prosperous. They could worship the one true God in their own way. They could follow their old, old customs. And they had become what they had long dreamed of and struggled for—an independent nation.

When Simon grew too old to serve as general, he called his two oldest sons, John and Judas, to him. He said to them: "I and my brothers and the house of my father have fought the wars of Israel from our youth until this day, and things have prospered in our hands so that we have delivered Israel many times. But now I have grown old, and you by His mercy are mature in years. Take my place and my brother's and go out and fight for our nation, and may the help which comes from Heaven be with you." And the sons went out and fought for Israel.

Simon had appointed his son-in-law governor over the plain of Jericho. The man was ambitious, and determined to get control of the whole country. He invited his father-in-law, Simon, and two of his brothers-in-law to a great banquet, and there he had them killed. Then the wicked governor sent men to do away with his brother-in-law John, and he ordered other men to go and take possession of Jerusalem.

But John had been warned. He escaped from the men sent to kill him and reached Jerusalem ahead of those ordered by his evil brother-in-law to take the city. And in Jerusalem, John, called John Hyrcanus, became high priest and ruler of Judah, following his father Simon.

## A MYSTERIOUS FLAME

The Second Book of the Maccabees does not go on with the history given in the First Book, as one might expect from its title. It covers fewer years than 1 Maccabees, and says nothing at all about the leadership of Jonathan and Simon, for it ends with Judas' victory over Nicanor.

There is much less straightforward history in 2 Maccabees than in 1 Maccabees. 2 Maccabees is full of miracles, and dreams, and angels, and stories about the Jerusalem temple, and tales of Jews who died for their religion. Most of the book, the author says, is based on a five-volume history by a man named Jason.

2 Maccabees begins with two letters, both of them from the Jews in Palestine to the Jews in Egypt. Each letter urges the Jews in Egypt to keep the feast of the dedication of the temple (*Hannukah*) at the same time it is celebrated in Jerusalem. In the second letter this story of the mysterious flame is told.

At the time that Jerusalem was captured by the Babylonians, Jeremiah was the prophet or spokesman for God to the Jews. Before the people of Jerusalem were led away as slaves, Jeremiah ordered the temple priests to take a spark of the sacred fire from the holy altar and to hide it. They did this, putting the fire among the stones of a dry cistern in so safe and so secret a place that no one went to it for many years.

About fifty years after the Jews were led off to Babylonia, the city of Babylon was captured by the Persians. Nehemiah, one of the Jews of Babylon, gained the confidence of the Persian king and received his permission to help the Jewish people.

One of the first things Nehemiah did was to have the sacred altar fire relighted. He sent descendants of the priests who had hidden the fire to get a spark of the sacred flame.

These priests went at once to the dry cistern and searched among the stones for the fire. To their dismay they found no spark at all, and no sign of any flame. All they discovered was a thick black liquid. Disappointed, they went back to Nehemiah and told him of their unsuccessful search.

Nehemiah was still hopeful. He asked the priests to return to the place, dip out some of the black liquid, and bring it to the outdoor altar.

The priests went back to the dry cistern. They dipped out some of the black liquid and brought it to the altar, where they sprinkled it over the sacrifice lying there. The people gathered around and watched. Nehemiah watched, too, and so did the priests.

For a time nothing happened. Then the sun, which had been under a cloud, came out and shone brightly on the altar. All at once a fire blazed up. The people gazed, spellbound, as it flared and burned higher and higher until it completely consumed the sacrifice on the altar. While it burned, the priests prayed to God, praising him and singing hymns of thanksgiving. "Accept this sacrifice on behalf of all thy people Israel," they begged.

When the sacrifice was entirely consumed, Nehemiah told the priests to take the liquid that was left and pour it over some large stones. A flame blazed up from the stones, but when the light from the altar shone upon it, the fire went out.

Nehemiah told the Persian king about the strange liquid. The king found the story hard to believe and sent men to investigate the matter. When they reported that Nehemiah's story was true, the king gave orders that the hollow where the black liquid had been found should be enclosed and marked to show it was a sacred place.

Nehemiah called the black liquid *nephthar,* which means cleansing. Most of the people called it naphtha—the name still used for it.

## THE ARMORED RIDER

**This miracle-story is told in the third chapter of 2 Maccabees.**

Many years after Nehemiah's time, Palestine came under the rule of the Syrian kings. One of these kings was badly in need of money to carry on his wars. Someone reported to him that the Jews had so much money in their temple in Jerusalem that they could not even count it. The Syrian king rubbed his hands greedily and decided to seize that money. He called in Heliodorus, one of his high officials whom he trusted, and ordered him to go to Jerusalem and get the money from the temple treasury.

Heliodorus went at once to Jerusalem. There he hurried to Onias, the high priest, and told him why he had come to the city. He asked the high priest bluntly if the report about the great sums of money in the temple treasury were true.

Onias told Heliodorus that there were some personal sums of money in the temple treasury in addition to the temple funds. These had been left there for safekeeping by widows and orphans and a few others. Onias explained that this money could not possibly be given to the king. Such a deed would be unjust to the people who had trustingly brought their money to the temple. It would also be unjust to the temple, for it would hurt its good name, held in honor the world over.

But Heliodorus had an order from the king and was determined to obey that order. So he set a day on which he would come to the temple to direct the matter of counting and taking the money.

When the people of Jerusalem heard the news, they were frantic. All over the city groups gathered to talk about it. In their distress they cried aloud and raised their hands to heaven, calling upon God to protect his holy place. At the temple, priests knelt before the altars in prayer. The high priest looked like a man stricken; his body trembled and his gray face showed the pain within his heart.

On the appointed day Heliodorus went to the temple. With him were his helpers and his bodyguard. Onias waited for them in the temple treasury.

As Heliodorus and his men marched toward the door of the treasury, their way was suddenly blocked by a magnificent horse which appeared before them. On its back sat a rider clad in armor and bearing weapons of gold. Numb with terror, the men stood motionless.

With a rush the horse sprang toward Heliodorus and struck out at him with its two front hoofs. At the same time two strong, handsome young men appeared, splendidly dressed. Standing one on each side of Heliodorus, they began to strike and beat him.

Heliodorus, terror-stricken and wounded, lost consciousness and fell to the temple floor. As soon as his men could gather their wits, they picked him up and carried him out. He was speechless and helpless and seemed near death.

The high priest and all those in the temple breathed a great sigh of relief that their treasury had not been entered. In their joy they cried aloud and thanked God for saving the honor of his temple.

In the midst of their rejoicing, some of Heliodorus' friends came hurrying in to the high priest. They begged him to pray to the Most High to spare the life of Heliodorus. The high priest agreed to do this and even to offer a sacrifice for Heliodorus' recovery.

While the high priest was making the sacrifice, the

two young men who had beaten Heliodorus appeared again to the stricken man. "Be very grateful to Onias the high priest," they said, "since for his sake the Lord has granted you your life."

When Heliodorus regained his strength he, too, offered sacrifice to the Lord and made vows to serve him. Then, fully recovered, he left Jerusalem with his men and journeyed back to Syria.

There Heliodorus told the king his experience. The king, who still wanted the money, asked Heliodorus to suggest the kind of man he could send to Jerusalem to do what he had ordered.

"If you have any enemy or plotter against your government," Heliodorus answered, "send him there, for you will get him back thoroughly scourged, if he escapes at all, for there certainly is about the place some power of God. For he who has his dwelling in heaven watches over that place himself and brings it aid, and he strikes and destroys those who come to do it injury."

The king thought over what Heliodorus had said. Regretfully he gave up his idea. He made no more attempts to get money from the Jerusalem temple treasury; and Onias, the high priest, was left in peace.

## WISE SAYINGS AND GOOD ADVICE

Wise men were highly respected in ancient Palestine, as they were in all eastern countries. The stories they told, and the witty and wise remarks they made, were sometimes collected and written down. In this way they would endure for more than the length of one lifetime and could be enjoyed by many more people. The Old Testament Book of Proverbs is such a collection, and there are several books of this sort in the Apocrypha.

King Solomon, David's son, was supposed to have been

the wisest man of all time. Many centuries after Solomon died, a Jewish scholar set down his own words of wisdom as if King Solomon were speaking. He hoped that by calling his book The Wisdom of Solomon more people would read it. And so, no doubt, they did. The Apostle Paul was influenced by it, and many scholars of the early Christian church thought The Wisdom of Solomon the most important and beautiful book of the Apocrypha.

Here are a few selections from it.

"Wisdom is radiant and unfading,
and she is easily discerned by those
    who love her,
and is found by those who seek her.
She hastens to make herself known
    to those who desire her."

"For she is a reflection of eternal light,
a spotless mirror of the working of God,
and an image of his goodness."

"God loves nothing so much as
    the man who lives with wisdom."

A second and much longer Apocrypha book of wisdom is often called Sirach, after the name of the author's father. Its full title is Ecclesiasticus, or The Wisdom of Jesus the

Son of Sirach. The word Ecclesiasticus shows the connection of this Apocrypha book with the early Christian church, where it was used as a sort of textbook on the good life.

Sirach is one of the few books in either the Old Testament or the Apocrypha where the author's name is really known. The writer of the introduction tells us that he inherited the book, which had been written in Hebrew by his grandfather in Jerusalem fifty years before. The grandfather's name was Jesus, quite a common name among the Jews. The father of Jesus was called Sirach, and so this Jesus was also called Ben Sirach, meaning the son of Sirach.

Ben Sirach was a scholar, a traveler, a lecturer, and a teacher, with a little private school of his own in Jerusalem. In his book he had set down some of his classroom lessons, his lectures, and his thoughts about the goodness and the greatness of God. He had also set down his ideas about the right way for people to live and get along with one another, and the ways they should behave on different occasions.

This book seemed so valuable to the learned man's grandson that he felt he should translate it into Greek. He wanted the Greek-reading Jews of Alexandria and other places to have a chance to know it and profit by its teachings. In his introduction he begged readers to excuse any blunders he had made in translation. It had not been easy, he said, to find just the right Greek words to give the true meaning to his grandfather's Hebrew sentences.

The grandson was right in thinking that the book was well worth translating. Sirach became very popular among the Jews both within and without Palestine. Later scholars called it the brightest gem of the Apocrypha. It was highly treasured by early Christians, and for centuries was used in the Church. Even today those who read the words of Ben Sirach find them as full of truth and common sense as when he wrote them in Jerusalem, nearly two hundred years before Christ.

Here are some of Ben Sirach's wise sayings:

"All wisdom comes from the Lord
    and is with him for ever."

"If you desire wisdom, keep the commandments,
    and the Lord will supply it for you."

"Do not refrain from speaking at the crucial time,
    and do not hide your wisdom.
For wisdom is known through speech,
    and education through the words of the tongue."

"Strive even to death for the truth
    and the Lord God will fight for you."

"Be quick to hear,
    and be deliberate in answering."

"There is nothing so precious as a faithful friend."

"A man's heart changes his countenance,
  either for good or for evil.
The mark of a happy heart
  is a cheerful face."

"Never repeat a conversation,
  and you will lose nothing at all. . . .
Have you heard a word? Let it die with you.
  Be brave! It will not make you burst!"

"A slip on the pavement is better
  than a slip of the tongue."

"It is ill-mannered for a man to listen at a door."

"Are you seated at the table of a great man?
  Do not be greedy at it, . . .
Do not reach out your hand for everything you see,
  and do not crowd your neighbor at the dish."

"Not everything is good for every one,
  and not every person enjoys everything."

"Kindness is like a garden of blessings,
  and almsgiving endures for ever."

"The glory of the stars is the beauty of heaven,

a gleaming array in the heights of the Lord.
At the command of the Holy One they stand as ordered,
  they never relax in their watches.
Look upon the rainbow, and praise him who made it,
  exceedingly beautiful in its brightness.
It encircles the heaven with its glorious arc;
  the hands of the Most High have stretched it out."


"Though we speak much we cannot reach the end,
  and the sum of our words is: 'He is the all.'
Where shall we find strength to praise him?
  For he is greater than all his works."


Baruch was the friend and secretary of the prophet
Jeremiah. It was in his time that the people of Jerusalem
were driven out of their city and led away as captives to
Babylonia.

The book of Baruch may not have been written by
Baruch but merely named in honor of him. This was a
common custom in those times. Very likely Baruch was
written in a later time of trouble and persecution. Because
it seemed to be about the days of the Jews' captivity in
Babylonia, the scroll of Baruch could be read openly by
the Jews who lived under the Romans. Roman officials
would not bother to substitute Roman names for the
Babylonian ones. Only the Jewish readers of Baruch
would know that this should be done and would find
comfort and advice in its words.

These passages are from Baruch:

"Let thy anger turn away from us, for we are left, few
in number, among the nations where thou hast scattered
us. Hear, O Lord, our prayer and supplication, and for
thy own sake deliver us, and grant us favor in the sight
of those who have carried us into exile; that all the earth
may know that thou art the Lord our God."

"You have forsaken the fountain of wisdom.
If you had walked in the way of God,
    you would be dwelling in peace for ever.
Learn where there is wisdom,
    where there is strength,
    where there is understanding,
that you may at the same time discern
    where there is length of days, and life,
    where there is light for the eyes, and peace."

"Take courage, my children, cry to God,
        and he will deliver you from the power
        and hand of the enemy."

"For God will lead Israel with joy,
    in the light of his glory,
    with the mercy and righteousness
    that come from him."

Following the book of Baruch in the Apocrypha is a short letter named for the prophet Jeremiah. In some versions of the Apocrypha this letter is printed as part of the book of Baruch, perhaps because Jeremiah and Baruch were close friends. Usually, even if it is printed as a separate book, the letter is numbered as the sixth and last chapter of Baruch. Sometimes it is called The Epistle of Jeremy. Jeremy is the Greek form of the name Jeremiah. No one knows who actually wrote the letter, which is really a short lecture on the foolishness of worshiping foreign gods and idols. These passages are from The Letter of Jeremiah:

"Now in Babylon you will see gods made of silver and gold and wood, which are carried on men's shoulders and inspire fear in the heathen. So take care not to become at all like the foreigners or to let fear for these gods possess you, when you see the multitude before and behind them worshiping them. But say in your heart, 'It is thou, O Lord, whom we must worship.'"

"The gods of the heathen . . . do not notice when their faces have been blackened by the smoke of the temple. Bats, swallows, and birds light on their bodies and heads; and so do cats. From this you will know that they are not gods; so do not fear them."

"Gods made of wood and overlaid with silver and gold

are not able to save themselves from thieves and robbers. Strong men will strip them of their gold and silver and of the robes they wear, and go off with this booty, and they will not be able to help themselves. . . . Therefore one must not think that they are gods nor call them gods, for they are not able either to decide a case or to do good to men. Since you know then that they are not gods, do not fear them."

## A PRAYER OF REPENTANCE

The Old Testament Second Book of Chronicles and Second Book of Kings tells of the long reign of King Manasseh and the thirty-third chapter of II Chronicles mentions his prayer of repentence. This, it says, was written down in the *Chronicles of the Seers,* which is one of the lost books of ancient Jewish history. In early Christian times a copy of the prayer of Manasseh was found. Some scholars think it was written by a Jewish priest at the time of the Maccabees. But it sounds as if it were actually spoken by a very repentant King.

King Manasseh ruled over Judah from the time he was

107

twelve until he was nearly seventy years old. He did all sorts of evil things. He built altars to foreign gods and even set them up in the house of the Lord. In many ways he encouraged the people of Israel to forget God's laws.

God warned Manasseh, but he paid no heed. At last he was captured and bound with heavy chains and led captive into a faraway country. There King Manasseh repented of his wickedness. He prayed to God to forgive him. And he prayed so humbly and sincerely that God heard his prayer. God forgave the repentant king and restored his kingdom to him.

This is a part of The Prayer of Manasseh:

"And now I bend the knee of my heart,
    beseeching thee for thy kindness.
I have sinned, O Lord, I have sinned,
    and I know my transgressions.
I earnestly beseech thee,
    forgive me, O Lord, forgive me! . . .
    and I will praise thee continually
        all the days of my life.
For all the host of heaven sings thy praise,
    and thine is the glory for ever. Amen."

# ABOUT THE APOCRYPHA

## ABOUT THE APOCRYPHA

Long, long ago there was a highway leading through
Palestine, the little country of the Hebrews, now called
Israel. This highway connected the lands of the east with
the countries on the Great Sea—the Mediterranean. Car-
avans, like the one which took Joseph to Egypt, went
over it. Armies from Egypt marched along it and so did
armies marching westward from the eastern countries of
Assyria and Babylonia.

The glorious days of King David and King Solomon
were followed by a rebellion in Palestine, and the Hebrew nation divided itself into two kingdoms. They were

called Israel and Judah. After two hundred years (about 720 B.C.) the northern kingdom of Israel was conquered by the Assyrians. Most of its people were led away eastward over the great highway and settled in faraway places. They never saw their homeland again.

A little more than a hundred years later Judah, the small southern kingdom of Palestine, was conquered by the Babylonians and many of its people were led along that same highway eastward to Babylonia. Fifty years passed. Then Cyrus, king of Persia, conquered Babylonia. And King Cyrus decreed that any of the captive Hebrews who wished to return to Judah might do so. They were free to rebuild their city of Jerusalem and their temple— the magnificent temple of Solomon which the Babylonians had destroyed.

The Judeans, or Jews, who returned to Jerusalem were full of thanksgiving to God. Their scribe Ezra read to them the sacred Hebrew books of religion and history, treasured from the time of Moses. Parts of these books were so old that they had been handed down by word of mouth from one generation to another. Then, probably in David's time, they had been written on rolls of dried, smoothed-out animal skins, cut into long strips, and called scrolls.

The people of Judah (or Judea) accepted these sacred books as the foundation of their nation. They became its constitution and its law. These Hebrew scriptures, called the law, were the first five books of our Bible—Genesis,

Exodus, Leviticus, Numbers, and Deuteronomy.

After two more centuries had passed, about two hundred years before Christ, the sayings of the Hebrew holy men, the spokesmen for God called prophets, were also accepted as part of the Hebrew scriptures. These had long before been set down on scrolls. They were divided into two parts: The Former Prophets (Joshua, Judges, Samuel, Kings) and The Latter Prophets (Isaiah, Jeremiah, Ezekiel, and The Twelve).

These scrolls of the prophets formed the second part of the Jews' sacred scriptures, which were often called the law and the prophets. Jesus spoke of the sacred books many times this way, and he read from the "roll of the prophet Isaiah" in the little Nazareth synagogue.

Besides the law and the prophets there were other religious writings which were used in the synagogue services. There were the psalms, which the people sang, the wise sayings called proverbs, the story poem of Job, some books of history, and some stories which were read on feast days. Gradually these other writings came to be regarded as a part of the Hebrew sacred scriptures. But for a long time this third part of the Hebrew Bible, spoken of as the writings, was not so definite as the other two parts—the law and the prophets.

The four hundred years between the Old and New Testaments is sometimes called the silent period. Yet this time was really a very active and important time for the Jews. During these years they were growing and developing in their religious beliefs and in the firmness of their faith in the One God. They were thinking more and more about the laws given them by Moses so long before and were trying to follow these laws more closely in their daily life. The Jews' ideas about such things as eternal life, and the Messiah, and their place as the special people of God grew broader and firmer. Synagogues sprang up all over Palestine, and far beyond its borders. Wherever there were Jews, there were synagogues. In them teachers and scholars explained the law and directed the thinking both of adults and of children.

For a while after their return from captivity things had gone along fairly well for the Jews in Palestine. Then, along with the larger countries to the east and Egypt also, Palestine was conquered by Alexander the Great. The rulers who followed Alexander forced the Greek way of life on the conquered peoples everywhere. They persecuted the Jews who clung to their old customs and religion. In the century or two before Jesus' birth, under Syrian and then Roman rulers, times were especially bad in Palestine. There were high taxes and persecution and famines.

For a long time Jews had been going to other countries to live. As times grew harder, more and more of them moved away from Palestine. Most of the Jews journeyed to the north or west, to settle in Asia Minor or Greece or Egypt or Italy. By New Testament times there were almost as many Jews living in these countries as in Palestine.

And every large community had its synagogue with its weekly interpretation of the law and its daily school for boys.

There was an especially large number of Jews in the great city of Alexandria, in Egypt. Like the rest of the people there, they spoke Greek and were deeply influenced by Greek ways of thinking and living. Most of the younger Jews could not read or understand Hebrew, the ancient language of the Jews and the one in which their sacred scriptures were written. They did not even know the Aramaic language, which was spoken by the common people of Palestine. And so it became important to have the Hebrew scriptures translated into Greek, the language most used by the Jewish people outside Palestine.

The story is told of seventy (or perhaps seventy-two) learned men being invited to come from Jerusalem to Alexandria to prepare a Greek Bible. This was called the *Septuagint,* in honor of these seventy (or seventy-two) men who worked so hard and well to translate the Hebrew scriptures into Greek.

Jewish religious scholars in Alexandria also worked on making this Greek Bible, the *Septuagint.* Little by little they added to the older Hebrew scriptures more recent historical and religious writings which they felt should be included in the new Bible. There were additions to the books of Daniel and Esther; there were prayers and hymns, visions, and historical accounts which were used in Jewish synagogues outside Palestine. Some of these scrolls were written in Hebrew, some in Aramaic, and some in Greek. Gradually more than a dozen of them came to be included in the *Septuagint,* the Greek Bible made in Egypt before Jesus' birth.

This was the Bible read by the Jews in all the Greek-speaking countries around the Mediterranean. Later it was used by the Jewish and Gentile (non-Jewish) members of the early Christian church. And when, largely because of Paul's missionary journeys, the Christian faith was taken over almost entirely by Gentiles, the *Septuagint* became their Bible.

In 90 A.D., Jewish religious leaders met at Jamnia in Palestine to make a final and official decision on exactly what should be included in the Hebrew Bible. There was no question about the law and the prophets, but there were many questions about which scrolls should be included in the third section of the scriptures—the writings. At this Council of Jamnia the Jewish religious leaders decided not to accept the extra books put into the *Septuagint* by the Jews of Alexandria. The Council decided that only writings whose authors had lived no later than the time of the latter prophets should be included in the Hebrew Bible.

Jewish people everywhere agreed to abide by this decision of the Council of Jamnia. And so, to this day, the Hebrew Bible is made up of the law, the prophets, and the writings agreed upon at that time—Psalms, Job,

116

Proverbs, the five "festal scrolls" (Ruth, the Song of Songs, Ecclesiastes, Lamentations, and Esther), and the historical books of Daniel, Ezra-Nehemiah, and Chronicles.

The Roman Empire grew stronger and stronger. Latin, instead of Greek, became the important language of the world. And so the Greek Bible needed to be translated into Latin. This was done several times during the second and third centuries after Christ, but always rather poorly. Toward the end of the fourth century the accepted leader of the Christians, the Pope, asked a great Christian scholar named Jerome to make a really good Latin Bible.

Jerome spent years doing this. He was not content just to patch up and improve the old Latin translations, or to make his translation from the Greek *Septuagint* alone. Jerome already knew the Greek language but he learned Hebrew and went to Palestine to get the help of Jewish scholars in his work. To make his Latin Bible as good as it could possibly be, he felt it should be based on the languages it had first been written in, as well as on Greek and Latin translations.

In Palestine Jerome found that many of the books which were in the Greek and Latin Bibles used by the Christian Church were not in the Hebrew scriptures at all. These extra, "outside" books he named the Apocrypha, which means hidden or secret. Jerome could find only two of these books—Tobit and Judith—in their old original language. With the help of Jewish scholars he

117

translated them into Latin. The others he retranslated from the Greek or from earlier Latin versions.

Jerome put into his new Latin Bible all these "outside" books found in the *Septuagint* but not in the Hebrew scriptures. He knew that the Christian Church leaders who had been using these books would continue to want them. He left them in the same places they had been in in the old Bibles, scattered through the latter part of the Old Testament. But he added a note listing the books which were "outside" the Hebrew scriptures and saying that he did not consider them as highly inspired as the other books of the Old Testament.

This great Latin translation of Jerome's was called the *Vulgate,* because it was written in the Latin tongue which the common or "vulgar" people used. The *Vulgate* was used for hundreds of years, all over Europe, and the Bible used today in the Roman Catholic Church is based on it.

Early in the sixteenth century Martin Luther translated the Bible into German, so that it could be read by the common people of Germany. Like Jerome, Luther went back to the old Greek and Hebrew Bibles. Like Jerome, too, he thought the books called *Apocrypha,* while "not held equal to the sacred scriptures, nevertheless are useful and good to read," and he kept them in his German Bible. But instead of leaving these "outside" books in their separate places, Luther gathered them together in one group which he put at the end of the Old Testament.

The year after Luther's German Bible was published, Myles Coverdale translated the Bible into English. He wanted to do for the common people of England what Luther had done for the people of Germany, making it possible for them to read the scriptures in their own language. Coverdale followed Luther's example in placing the Apocrypha books between the Old and the New Testaments. And that is where they continued to appear in all the English Bibles that came after Coverdale's, except for the translation made for use in the Catholic Church. This Bible left the Apocrypha books scattered through the Old Testament, as they were in Jerome's *Vulgate* Bible, from which it was translated. The English translation ordered by King James, the great Authorized Version of 1611, followed Martin Luther's and the others' example and printed the fifteen Apocrypha books at the end of the Old Testament, though without any note.

When the Puritans became powerful in England they opposed including the Apocrypha in the Holy Bible. If these were "outside" books and not so sacred or highly inspired as the rest of the Bible, why include them at all? the Puritans asked. And they demanded that Bibles be published without the Apocrypha.

There was much argument. Many bishops and other religious leaders claimed that even if these extra books were not of quite such high inspiration, still the Apocrypha stood next to the scriptures in authority and should be included in all Bibles. But the Puritans were very insistent. And the printers naturally liked the idea of having fewer pages to print and bind into the Bibles they published.

And so Bibles began to appear without the Apocrypha, and gradually people became used to having them that way. The prayer books of the Anglican Church of England and the Episcopal Church continued to include readings from the Apocrypha. But during the eighteenth and nineteenth centuries, except for Catholic Bibles, Bibles containing the Apocrypha became more and more unusual. Even the large Bibles used in Protestant church pulpits were printed without the Apocrypha in them. Today a Bible with these "outside" books is so rare that many Protestants have not even seen such a Book.

During the first half of the twentieth century, however, and especially since the discovery of the Dead Sea Scrolls, there has been increased interest in the Apocrypha. After the new English translation known as the Revised Standard Version was finished a few years ago, the Division of Christian Education of the National Council of the Churches of Christ in the U.S.A. which had sponsored it, had many requests for a revised English translation of the Apocrypha to go along with the "R.S.V." And so a committee of scholars was organized and authorized to make such a translation. In 1957, *The Apocrypha of the Old Testament: Revised Standard Version* was published. It was "translated from the Greek and Latin tongues, being the version set forth A.D. 1611, revised A.D. 1894, compared with the most ancient authorities and revised A.D. 1957."

All quotations in *The Three Guardsmen and Other Stories from the Apocrypha* are from that book.

# APOCRYPHA QUOTATIONS

## The Three Guardsmen
Direct quotations from 1 Esdras 3:6-7; 3:10, 11, 12; 3: 16; 3:18, 22-24; 4:8-10, 12; 4:16-17, 20; 22, 31-32; 4:35, 38, 40; 4:41; 4:42; 4:46; 4: 58-60; 4:63; 5:2.

## Some Curious Visions
Direct quotations from 2 Esdras 4:3-4, 5, 6, 9, 10-11; 6:33; 12:46-47; 14:25-26; 14: 38, 39; 14:45-47; 16:52.

## The Strange Adventures of Tobias
Direct quotations from Tobit 2:2; 2:3; 2:13; 4:15; 4:21; 5:1-2; 5:3; 5:5; 5:6; 5: 7, 8; 5:11; 5:16; 5:21; 6:3, 4; 6:7-8; 6:10-12; 6:14; 6:15, 16-17; 7:2, 3, 4, 5, 7, 10, 11, 18; 8:16-17; 10:12; 11:6, 17; 12: 2, 3, 4, 5, 7-8, 14, 17-18, 20; 14:13.

## The Daring Deed of a Beautiful Woman
Direct quotations from Judith 2:5-6; 5:3-4; 5:21; 7: 30-31; 8:11-12, 15, 24, 31, 32-

34; 9:9, 11; 10:8, 9; 10:13, 19; 11:1-3, 10, 11, 12, 13, 16, 19, 21, 22-23; 12:2, 3, 4, 17, 18; 13:7, 11, 15; 14:18; 15:9, 10; 16:2, 13, 25.

## Queen Esther Goes Before the King
Direct quotations from the Additions to the Book of Esther 11:7, 10-11; 13:17; 14: 2, 12-13, 14, 19; 15:3-5, 7, 8.

## Susanna and the Two Evil Elders
Direct quotations from Susanna 13, 20, 21, 23, 35, 36-37, 39, 48-49, 52-53, 54, 58.

## Daniel and Bel
Direct quotations from Bel and the Dragon 5, 6, 7, 8-9, 12, 17, 18, 19, 20.

## Daniel and the Dragon
Direct quotations from Bel and the Dragon 24, 25, 26, 27, 29, 34, 35, 37, 41.

## In the Fiery Furnace
Direct quotations from the

Prayer of Azariah and the Song of the Three Young Men 22, 35, 67-68.

**The Story of a Brave Family**
Direct quotations from 1 Maccabees 2:17-18, 19-20, 22, 27; 3:19, 21, 58; 4:54, 56, 58, 59; 8:12, 31-32; 9:10; 13:5, 9; 14:11-12, 43; 16:2-3.

**A Mysterious Flame**
Direct quotation from 2 Maccabees 1:26.

**The Armored Rider**
Direct quotations from 2 Maccabees 3:33, 38-39.

**Wise Sayings and Good Advice**
Direct quotations from the Wisdom of Solomon: 6:12-13; 7:26; 7:28.
Sirach 1:1, 26; 4:23-24, 28; 5:11; 6:15; 13:25-26; 19:7, 10; 20:18; 21:24; 31:12, 14; 37:28; 40:17; 43:9-12, 27-28.
Baruch 2:13-15; 3:12-14; 4:21; 5:9.
The Letter of Jeremiah: 6:4-6; 17, 20-23; 57-58, 64-65.

**A Prayer of Repentance**
Direct quotations from The Prayer of Manasseh 11-13; 15.

# INDEX AND GUIDE TO PRONUNCIATION

## Pronunciation Key

a—as in fat, man, pang

ā—as in fate, mane, dale

ä—as in far, father, guard

à—as in ask, fast, ant

e—as in met, pen, bless

ē—as in mete, meet

i—as in pin, it

ī—as in pine, fight, file

o—as in not, on, frog

ō—as in note, poke, floor

ö—as in move, spoon

ô—as in nor, song, off

u—as in hub

ū—as in mute, acute

ü—as in prune

′ indicates accented syllable

124

125

128